MULTIPLE-CHOICE AND FREE-RESPONSE QUESTIONS IN PREPARATION FOR THE AP BIOLOGY EXAMINATION

(SIXTH EDITION)

By

Glenn Hartman
Archmere Academy
Claymont, Delaware

and

Jennifer Pfannerstill
Tomahawk High School
Tomahawk, Wisconsin

D&S MARKETING SYSTEMS, INC.
1205 38th Street • Brooklyn, NY 11218

w w w . d s m a r k e t i n g . c o m

ISBN # 978-1-934780-22-0 / 1-934780-22-7

Printed in the U.S.A.

Preface

The newly designed College Board Advanced Placement Biology Examination consists of 63 multiple-choice questions, 6 grid-in numerical questions, 2 long free-response questions and 6 short free-response questions. The multiple-choice questions have four answer choices and will require students to analyze data, draw conclusions, apply relevant knowledge and perform calculations. The grid-in questions will involve graphs, data, experimental or content analysis that can end with a numerical answer. The numerical answer must be filled into grids on a scantron sheet. At 10 points each, the long free-response questions will require students to connect many related biological topics into a larger thematic structure. At 2 to 6 points each, the smaller free-response questions will be more focused questions that require one to two paragraph responses that are directed about a specific topic.

The newly designed biology curriculum organizes the biological content and the mathematical and experimental applications into four Big Ideas. These Big Ideas serve as a way to draw links between related biological content. There are also a list of science practices that students are expected to be able to demonstrate in their test answers.

This book is intended to provide students and teachers with a comprehensive set of review materials to help students prepare for the multiple-choice portion of the exam as well as the free-response section of the exam. This edition consists of review material, organized into four Big Ideas, with thirty multiple-choice questions and a three to five free-response questions organized around each of the four Big Ideas. There are also three full-length practice examinations.

The Teacher's Manual contains complete explanations for each sample question which can be shared with students at the teacher's discretion, as well as rubrics for the free-response questions in the book. These descriptions are available for the complete tests and for the questions associated with each Big Idea.

The writing of this 6th edition of the AP biology review book has been a very rewarding process. We would both like to recognize our families for their support and generous giving of time to allow for the creation of this document, our current and past students who patiently tried out many questions, and all of our AP reader friends.

All communications concerning this book should be addressed to:

D&S Marketing Systems, Inc.
1205 38th Street
Brooklyn, NY 11218
www.dsmarketing.com

TABLE OF CONTENTS

AP Biology

Introduction

How can teachers and students use this review guide?

This review guide is divided into several sections within the teacher manual and student study guide. Due to the ever-changing nature of the AP Biology course and its redesign, this guide has been formatted to incorporate and follow the organization of the new AP biology curriculum and incorporate the suggested *Big Ideas* as the organizational framework. Within each of these *Big Ideas* identified by the College Board, there is specific content material. These content areas have been sorted to accompany appropriate *Big Ideas*. The guide serves to provide you with examples of how the concepts within the new AP Biology curriculum can be covered.

The content is preceded by a **boldfaced** conceptual statement designed to demonstrate a relationship within each theme. Within each section, there is a:

- content review section of essential knowledge, organized in a conceptual way to maximize student understanding and teacher presentation

- list of pertinent vocabulary and phrases

- set of thought provoking multiple choice and free response questions of all types and answers to the questions (teacher's manual only), modeling those that will be on the AP© Examination

- reiteration of what is beyond the scope and sequence of the revised AP© *Biology* course

- suggestion of how the *Big Idea* relates to other *Big Ideas*, and how students may be asked to use knowledge from two or more areas to formulate responses and apply their knowledge to scenarios they may not be familiar with

- identification of what underlying content and processes must be taught.

There are also three full-length exams with annotated answers (teacher's manual only) at the conclusion of the book. By omitting the answers in the student manual, teachers may choose to use the questions as an assessment tool. However, teachers may also choose to provide those answers to their students, thus providing context for the content material. Students and teachers alike can benefit from the annotated answers.

What is AP Biology?

The course in AP Biology is designed to be a college level survey in biological sciences, touching on the mainstays of biological science by using a thematic approach.

At the beginning of the 2012-13 academic year, teachers of AP Biology will need to implement, if they have not already, several key components of the *new* AP Biology course, as articulated by The College Board. After many years of work, the following changes to the AP Biology curriculum have been delineated:

There is an increased emphasis placed on conceptual knowledge and understanding of biological concepts. Teachers will be encouraged to engage students in inquiry labs instead of focusing on all of the many cases where structure relates to function throughout biology. Teachers may focus efforts on the conceptual understanding of that driving theme, and a few examples to support it. The College Board is supporting this by reducing the scope of content in AP Biology, allowing teachers to spend more time on conceptual understanding instead of memorizing every vocabulary term in the textbook.

There is an increased emphasis on scientific process as an essential skill. Teachers will encourage students to experiment, to apply reasoning skills and be the center of the investigation instead of offering step by step protocols, which they forget by the next day, and many times do not understand the purpose of each step in the procedure. Students will hypothesize, and be wrong sometimes, but this will increase their understanding of the topic and create a deeper knowledge than lecture and demonstration ever can do. This is all with the understanding that inquiry based learning ***must*** start in the elementary grades. Students must be accustomed to being asked the "how" and the "why" of biological phenomena, and this only happens with practice.

These definitive changes to the AP Biology curriculum are supported by the fact that the College Board has provided a concise and clear curriculum framework and set of learning objectives for AP Biology.

The AP Biology course is being broken into four ***Big Ideas***, the main themes in biology, which include Evolution, Cellular Processes, Genetics and Information Transfer, and Ecology. Within each Big Idea, there are ***Enduring Understandings*** that break that Big Ideas down into smaller parts. These are the core concepts within each Big Idea. These Enduring Understandings will address each of the relevant content areas associated with that Big Idea. There are also ***Essential Knowledge*** elements that are pieces of content that link that Enduring Understandings and Big Ideas together. These elements are important to understand concepts as they relate across the scope of biology. There are also ***Learning Objectives*** that describe what students should know. These are important in providing the basis for the exam questions. And finally, there are ***Science Practices***, which tie the content knowledge in the Essential Understandings to actually "doing" science and testing a hypothesis.

Big Idea #1: **The process of evolution drives the diversity and unity of life.**

Enduring Understandings	Essential Knowledge
1.A: Change in the genetic makeup of a population over time is evolution.	1.A.1: Natural selection is a major mechanism of evolution.
	1.A. 2: Natural selection acts on phenotypic variations in populations.
	1.A. 3: Evolutionary change is also driven by random processes.
	1.A. 4: Biological evolution is supported by scientific evidence from many disciplines, including mathematics.
1.B: Organisms are linked by lines of descent from common ancestry.	1.B.1: Organisms share many conserved core processes and features that evolved and are widely distributed among organisms today.
	1.B.2: Phylogenetic trees and cladograms are graphical representations of evolutionary history that can be tested.
1.C: Life continues to evolve within a changing environment.	1.C.1: Speciation and extinction have occurred throughout the Earth's history.
	1.C. 2: Speciation may occur when two populations become reproductively isolated from each other.
	1.C.3: Populations of organisms continue to evolve.
1.D: The origin of living systems is explained by natural processes.	1.D.1: There are several hypotheses about the natural origin of life on Earth, each with supporting scientific evidence.
	1.D.2: Scientific evidence from many different disciplines supports models of the origin of life

Big Idea #2: **Biological systems utilize energy and molecular building blocks to grow, to reproduce, and to maintain homeostasis**

Enduring Understandings	Essential Knowledge
2.A: Growth, reproduction and maintenance of the organization of living systems require free energy and matter.	2.A.1: All living systems require constant input of free energy.
	2.A.2: Organisms capture and store free energy for use in biological processes.
	2.A.3: Organisms must exchange matter with the environment to grow, reproduce and maintain organization.
2.B: Growth, reproduction and dynamic homeostasis require that cells create and maintain internal environments that are different from their external environments.	2.B.1: Cell membranes are selectively permeable due to their structure.
	2.B.2: Growth and dynamic homeostasis are maintained by constant movement of molecules across membranes.
	2.B.3: Eukaryotic cells maintain internal membranes that partition the cell into specialized regions.
2.C: Organisms use feedback mechanisms to regulate growth and reproduction, and to maintain dynamic homeostasis.	2.C.1: Organisms use feedback mechanisms to maintain their internal environments and respond to external environmental changes.
	2.C.2: Organisms respond to changes in the external environments.
2.D: Growth and dynamic homeostasis of a biological system are influenced by changes in the system's environment.	2.D.1: All biological systems from cells and organisms to populations, communities and ecosystems are affected by complex biotic and abiotic interactions involving exchange of matter and free energy.
	2.D.2: Homeostatic mechanisms reflect both common ancestry and divergence due to adaptation in different environments.
	2.D.3: Biological systems are affected by disruptions to their dynamic homeostasis.
	2.D.4: Plants and animals have a variety of chemical defenses against infections that affect dynamic homeostasis.

2.E: Many biological processes involved in growth, reproduction and dynamic homeostasis include temporal regulation and coordination.	2.E.1: Timing of coordination of specific events are necessary for the normal development of an organism, and these events are regulated by a variety of mechanisms.
	2.E.2: Timing and coordination of physiological events are regulated by multiple mechanisms.
	2.E.3: Timing and coordination of behavior are regulated by various mechanisms and are important in natural selection.

Big Idea #3: **Living systems store, retrieve, transmit, and respond to information essential to life processes.**

Enduring Understandings	Essential Knowledge
3.A: Heritable information provides for continuity of life.	3.A.1: DNA, and in some cases RNA, is the primary source of heritable information.
	3.A.2: In eukaryotes, heritable information is passed to the next generation via processes that include the cell cycle and mitosis or meiosis plus fertilization.
	3.A.3: The chromosomal basis of inheritance provides an understanding of the pattern of passage of genes from parent to offspring.
	3.A.4: The inheritance pattern of may traits cannot be explained by simple Mendelian genetics.
3.B: Expression of genetic information involves cellular and molecular mechanisms.	3.B.1: Gene regulation results in differential gene expression, leading to cell specialization.
	3.B.2: A variety of intercellular and intracellular signal transmissions mediate gene expression.
3.C: The processing of genetic information is imperfect and is a source of genetic variation.	3.C.1.Changes in genotypes can result in changes in phenotypes.
	3.C.2: Biological systems have multiple processes that increase genetic variation.
	3.C.3: Viral replication results in genetic variation, and viral infection can introduce genetic variation into hosts.
3.D: Cells communicate by generating, transmitting and receiving chemical signals.	3.D.1: Cell communication processes share common features that reflect a shared evolutionary history.
	3.D.2: Cells communicate with each other through direct contact with other cells or from a distance via chemical signaling.
	3.D.3: Signal transduction pathways link signal reception with cellular response.
	3.D.4: Changes in signal transduction pathways can alter cellular response.

3.E: Transmission of information results in changes within and between biological systems.	3.E.1: Individuals can act on information and communicate it to others.
	3.E.2: Animals have nervous systems that detect external and internal signals, transmit and integrate information, and produce responses.

Big Idea #4: **Biological systems interact, and these interactions possess complex properties.**

Enduring Understandings	Essential Knowledge
4.A: Interactions within biological systems lead to complex properties.	4.A.1: The subcomponents of biological molecules and their sequence determine the properties of that molecule.
	4.A.2: The structure and function of subcellular components, and their interactions, provide essential cellular responses.
	4.A.3. Interactions between external stimuli and regulated gene expression result in specialization of cells, tissues, and organs.
	4.A.4: Organisms exhibit complex properties due to interactions between their constituent parts.
	4.A.5: Communities are composed of populations of organisms that interact in complex ways.
4.B: Competition and cooperation are important aspects of biological systems.	4.B.1: Interactions between molecules affect their structure and function.
	4.B.2: Cooperative interactions within organisms promote efficiency in the use of energy and matter.
	4.B.3: Interactions between and within populations influence patterns of species distribution and abundance.
	4.B.4: Distribution of local and global ecosystems changes over time.
4.C: Naturally occurring diversity among and between components within biological systems affects interactions with the environment.	4.C.1: Variation in molecular units provides cells with a wider range of functions.
	4.C.2: Environmental factors influence the expression of the genotype in an organism.
	4.C.3: The level of variation in a population affects population dynamics.
	4.C.4: The diversity of species within an ecosystem may influence the stability.

The approximate amount of time needed to cover each of the *Big Ideas* is expected to vary slightly from teacher to teacher. Based upon the unique needs of your students, you may need more or less time in one *Big Idea* based upon your teaching methods and the differentiation of your students. Approximate values for the percentage of time that may be spent within each *Big Idea* are included below.

Big Idea	Percentage
Big Idea #1: The process of evolution drives the diversity and unity of life.	15-17 %
Big Idea #2: Biological systems utilize energy and molecular building blocks to grow, to reproduce, and to maintain homeostasis	28-32%
Big Idea #3: Living systems store, retrieve, transmit, and respond to information essential to life processes.	27-31%
Big Idea #4: Biological systems interact, and these interactions possess complex properties.	20-25%

There are also seven *Science Practices* that are mandated by the curriculum. Students are expected to be able to use and apply these skills during the AP Biology exam. These seven *Science Practices* are listed below. Within each *Science Practice* there are several skills that are emphasized.

Within the framework of these *Big Ideas* of biology, students are expected to answer multiple-choice and free-response questions about these biological scenarios, using process skills identified below. Students are expected to learn the material, design and carry out lab activities, analyze data, and make graphical and statistical representations of data.

Science Practice 1: The student can use representations and models to communicate scientific phenomena and solve scientific problems.

1.1 The student can create representations and models of natural or man-made phenomena and systems in the domain.

1.2: The student can describe representations and models of natural or man-made phenomena and systems in the domain.

1.3: The student can refine representations and models of natural or man-made phenomena and systems in the domain.

1.4: The student can use representations and models to analyze situations or solve problems qualitatively and quantitatively.

1.5: The student can express key elements of natural phenomena across multiple representations in the domain.

Science Practice 2: The student can use mathematics appropriately.

2.1: The student can justify the selection of mathematical routines to solve problems.

2.2: The student can apply mathematical routines to quantities that describe natural phenomena.

2.3: The student can estimate numerically quantities that describe natural phenomena.

Science Practice 3: The student can engage in scientific questioning to extend thinking or to guide investigations within the context of the AP course.

3.1: The student can pose scientific questions.

3.2: The student can refine scientific questions.

3.3: The student can evaluate scientific questions.

Science Practice 4: The student can plan and implement data collection strategies appropriate to a particular scientific question.

4.1: The student can justify the selection of the kind of data needed to answer a particular scientific question.

4.2: The student can design a plan for collecting data to answer a particular scientific question.

4.3: The student can collect data to answer a particular scientific question.

4.4: The student can evaluate sources of data to answer a particular scientific question.

Science Practice 5: The student can perform data analysis and evaluation of evidence.

5.1 The student can analyze data to identify patterns or relationships.

5.2: The student can refine observations and measurements based on data analysis.

5.3: The student can evaluate the evidence provided by data sets in relation to a particular scientific question.

Science Practice 6: The student can work with scientific explanations and theories.

6.1: The student can justify claims with evidence.

6.2: The student can construct explanations of phenomena based on evidence produced through scientific practices.

6.3: The student can articulate the reasons that scientific explanations and theories are refined or replaced.

6.4: The student can make claims and predictions about natural phenomena based on scientific theories and models.

6.5: The student can evaluate alternative scientific explanations.

Science Practice 7: The student is able to connect and relate knowledge across various scales, concepts and representations in and across domains.

7.1: The student can connect phenomena and models across spatial and temporal scales.

7.2: The student can connect concepts in and across domains to generalize or extrapolate in and/or across *Enduring Understandings* and/or *Big Idea*.

Throughout this book, we have identified several of the content areas below and included these content areas with the relevant material in the *Big Ideas* framework. Content overlap will occur often. All biology content material is interdependent on other material. Most content areas can be linked to each of these *Big Ideas*. It is important to remember that while this is an objective based test, questions are designed to assess conceptual knowledge, not simply discrete facts. If teachers are able to emphasize these concepts and apply them to the curriculum framework, students will not only be more prepared for the test, they will become more knowledgeable scientists.

What is the AP Biology Exam?

The AP Biology Examination is taken in early May and consists of two parts. The first section is called the *Multiple-Choice and Grid-Ins* section and counts for 50% of the exam grade. It is composed of 63 multiple-choice questions and 6 *Grid-In* questions, which may include mathematical manipulation and or calculation. Students will write and bubble in numerated answer for these questions.

Students are not limited, as in many standardized tests, from looking at other portions of the multiple-choice section throughout the 90-minute testing period. However, once that section has been completed and time has expired, students will not have access to the multiple-choice section while the free-response portion of the exam is administered.

The second section of the exam is the ***Free-Response*** section and counts for the remaining 50% of the exam. This section is further divided into two sub-sections. The first sub-section consists of a few multi-part free-response questions, one of which connects to the lab experience. Students are allotted 20-25 minutes per question. The second sub-section consists of several single-part free-response questions, varying in length. Students are allotted between 3-10 minutes per question. There are a total of two long free-response questions and six shorter free-response questions.

Free-response questions very frequently have ***directional words*** in them that students should notice. These words tell the students exactly what type of knowledge, and therefore response, is required. ***Directional words*** include: describe, discuss, compare, contrast, explain, list, etc. Free-response questions are also usually designed in multiple parts. Unlike other AP exams, all free-response questions on the AP Biology Examination are graded; there is no choice. However, within each question, there may be individual choice to answer particular parts of a question.

Tips for Completing the Multiple-Choice Section:

1. Read each answer choice carefully. First, try to eliminate answer choices that are clearly wrong.

2. Use your strong content knowledge to select the most appropriate answer choice. Notice that more than one may be relevant to the topic, but always select the most appropriate.

3. Since there isn't any penalty for incorrect answers, make educated guesses when the answer is not clear.

4. Bring several number 2 pencils with very clean erasers. Extraneous markings on the scantron test can interfere with the accuracy of the scanning equipment.

5. New questions will require the integration of science and mathematics skills. Because of the emphasis on quantitative skills, calculators may be used during the exam.

Tips for Completing the Free-Response Section:

1. Read each question thoroughly. Pay close attention to the verbs in the questions: identify if you are supposed to **list, describe,** or **explain** something and then focus writing of the essay around that action.

2. Identify the various components to the question. Divide questions that have multiple parts into separate sections even if not specifically asked for in the question because it makes the reading of the essay easier and it easier to see how you addressed each section in your response.

3. Pay attention to words like **"and"** and **"or."** It is important to answer only as many sections or give as many examples as directed to provide. Do not provide extra examples when a set number is requested. If no limit on example numbers is provided, feel free to elaborate with additional examples.

4. If a question asks you to explain three of four terms, only explain three. Any information you give on a fourth term will not be awarded points and will only be consuming valuable time.

5. Write in blue or black pen. Pencil is hard to read. Colored ink is distracting and not as clear to the reader.

6. Use the best and clearest handwriting that you can. Readers do not want to have to reread a section of a response several times to prevent missing some point-worthy comments.

7. Points are given for valid information with explanations. So, elaborate on your responses with explanations and examples. Often single related-words or unexplained references will not be allocated any points.

8. Bulleted answers and lists will not be awarded points. However, refrain from writing verbose essays that reword the same comment several times. You do not need to waste time writing formal essay introductions and summaries. All of the detailed, well-explained points will be awarded for information in the body of a traditional essay.

9. Keep the responses focused. If a question or part of a question asks you to focus on a specific component of a topic, stay focused on that component. You will not receive points for additional information on the concept that are not requested in the question. For example, if a question asks you to describe how genetic variation occurs in meiosis, do not waste time describing every event of each phase of meiosis. That information is not directly related to the posed question and will not earn points and will again consume valuable time.

10. Understanding science process skills is important. For graphs, provide titles and clearly defined and labeled axes. For experimental designs, describe plausible examples with clearly noted controls and experimental groups, standard conditions, replication, and data collection and analysis.

How is the Exam graded?

Exams are given a holistic score of 1, 2, 3, 4, or 5 based on the student's multiple-choice score (50%) and free-response score (50%). In the multiple-choice section, students earn one point for each correctly answered multiple-choice question. The AP Examination is a "rights-only" scored exam and students are not penalized for leaving a question unanswered or having multiple-choice answers that are incorrect. The free-response portion of the exam is graded by trained readers who design standards by which to grade the exam and objectively and consistently apply the rubric to each response. Then, the Chief Faculty Consultant converts the exam grade to a holistic score of 1, 2, 3, 4, or 5 with 5 being extremely well qualified, 4 being well qualified, 3 being qualified, 2 being possibly qualified, and no recommendation for a score of 1.

BIG IDEA!

Big Idea #1: The process of evolution drives the diversity and unity of life

Key Terms for this section:

- □ adaptation
- □ adaptive radiation
- □ allele
- □ allopatric speciation
- □ analogous structures
- □ antibiotic resistance
- □ artificial selection
- □ bottleneck effect
- □ cladograms
- □ clade
- □ common ancestor
- □ convergent evolution
- □ directional selection
- □ disruptive selection
- □ divergent evolution

- □ emigration
- □ evolution
- □ fertility
- □ Founder effect
- □ gene flow
- □ gene pool
- □ genetic drift
- □ homologous structures
- □ hybrid
- □ immigration
- □ isolation types
- □ limited resources
- □ mutation
- □ natural selection
- □ outgroup

- □ phenotype
- □ phylogenetic tree
- □ population
- □ protobiont
- □ random mating
- □ reproductive isolation
- □ serial endosymbiosis
- □ sexual selection
- □ speciation
- □ species
- □ stabilizing selection
- □ sterility
- □ sympatric speciation
- □ variation
- □ vestigial organs
- □ viability

1

1.A Change in the genetic makeup of a population over time is evolution.

- **Natural selection is a major mechanism of evolution.**
- **Natural selection acts on phenotypic variations in populations.**
- **Evolutionary change is also driven by random processes.**
- **Biological evolution is supported by scientific evidence from many disciplines, including mathematics.**

Survival and reproduction are necessary to affect future generation's changes in allele frequencies.

- Ecosystems possess unique carrying capacities that address limited resources, competition, and reproductive potential. Organisms that survive and reproduce will pass on traits to the next generation.
- **Variation** occurs within a population and is heritable.
- Evolution occurs as traits accumulate in a population.
- The size of the gene pool affects the rate of **mutation**.

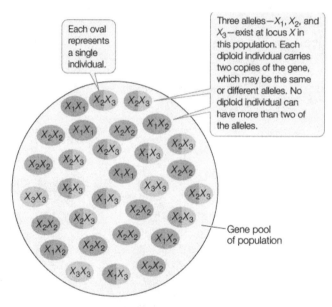

A Gene Pool, Hillis, Savada, Heller and Price. Principles of Life, 2012. Gordonsville, VA: W.H. Freeman & Co., 2012

Natural selection is a driving force for evolution and may act upon a population in a variety of ways.

- **Natural selection** describes a process where the organisms with the most favorable traits in an environment have an increased reproductive fitness.
- **Mutation** introduces new alleles. A mutation is an error in the DNA that happens during DNA replication or meiosis.
- **Emigration** and **immigration** impact allele frequency. As individuals move into or out of an area, it is called **gene flow**.

- **Genetic drift** can affect allele frequencies by random chance altering allele frequencies when populations are small. It often occurs following a bottleneck or founder effect.
- Mating patterns, such as **inbreeding** and **selection**, affect allele frequency.
- **Sexual selection** occurs when mating is not completely random. Individuals that are selected more often as mates will contribute more alleles to future generations than the less desirable mates.

Specific phenotypes provide adaptations to populations which make them more likely to survive and reproduce in a given ecosystem.

- **Stabilizing selection** favors individuals with intermediate phenotypes and extreme phenotypes are selected against; heterozygote advantage is an example of stabilizing selection
- **Directional selection** favors individuals with one extreme phenotype while the other extreme is selected against
- **Distruptive selection** favors the extreme phenotypes while the intermediate *phenotypes are selected against.*

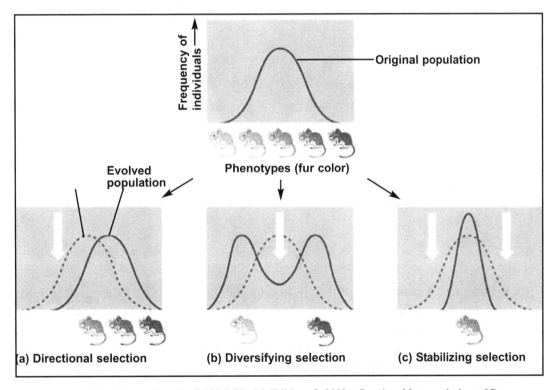

Campbell, Neil A. Reece; Jane B., BIOLOGY, 6th Edition, © 2002. Reprinted by permission of Pearson Education, Inc., Upper Saddle River, New Jersey.

Evolution follows several different patterns based upon different pressures.

- **Convergent evolution** occurs when two populations of dissimilar organisms evolve similar morphological traits because they are exposed to similar selection pressures.
- **Parallel evolution** is similar to convergent evolution, however the organisms do not need to occupy the same niches.
- **Divergent evolution** occurs when organisms have evolved new traits in their environments that cause them to phenotypically diverge from a common ancestor.
    - **Adaptive radiation** occurs as a species diverges across several different ecosystems.

Variation within a population is a necessary condition for natural selection to occur. This variation occurs through the following processes:

- Mutation
- Crossing over
- Random assortment
- Random fertilization
- Diploidy

The Hardy-Weinberg equilibrium provides a mathematical way to study the allele frequency changes within a population.

- If the following Hardy-Weinberg conditions are maintained, the population's allele and genotype frequencies will remain constant:
    - ✓ Large breeding population
    - ✓ Random mating
    - ✓ No mutation of alleles
    - ✓ No differential migration
    - ✓ No selection

- If A and a are alleles for a gene and each individual (diploid) carries two alleles, then p is the frequency of the A (dominant) allele and q is the frequency of the a (recessive) allele.
- Populations in genetic equilibrium are represented by the following equations:

$$p + q = 1.0\ (100\%)$$
$$p2 + 2pq + q2 = 1$$

where: p^2 = frequency of the homozygous dominant genotype

$2pq$ = frequency of the heterozygous genotype

q^2 = frequency of homozygous recessive genotype

Evidence for evolution spans several scientific disciplines and helps us to determine evolutionary relationships.

- Examination of the amino acid sequences of DNA through molecular biology techniques reveals that closely related species exhibit similar nucleotide sequences.
    - Closely related species share a higher percentage of the amino acid sequence than distantly related species.
- Structural similarities of body parts give rise to the understanding of evolutionary relationships.
    - Analogous structures: structures that appear similar in two unrelated organisms
    - Vestigial organs: organs that have no apparent function, but resemble ancestral structures
    - Homologous structures: structures with different apparent functions, but similar structural anatomy

Can you:

- ☐ identify the mechanisms of how variation occurs in a given population?

- ☐ explain how the effects of genetic drift vary based upon population size?

- ☐ discuss the different types of selection, and how each drives evolution?

- ☐ determine the frequency of the dominant allele if the frequency of the recessive allele is given?

- ☐ determine the frequency of the recessive allele if the percentage of the population with the recessive phenotype is given?

- ☐ calculate the percentage of the population with recessive allele if the percentage of the population expressing the dominant allele is given?

- ☐ differentiate between the frequency of an allele and the frequency of a genotype?

- ☐ interpret a graph showing how evolution favors different phenotypes?

- ☐ explain the changes in a gene pool as a result of emigration and immigration?

- ☐ explain how certain pressures can increase or decrease the fitness of a particular population?

1.B   Organisms are linked by lines of descent from common ancestry.

   • **Organisms share many conserved core processes and features that evolved and are widely distributed among organisms today.**
   • **Phylogenetic trees and cladograms are graphical representations of evolutionary history that can be tested.**

Similarities within the genetic code of all organisms support structural and functional similarities between organisms.

   • There are striking similarities between DNA, RNA and amino acids across all domains.

Specific cellular similarities support relatedness between organisms.

   • Cytoskeletal elements, membrane bound organelles including mitochondria and chloroplasts, chromosome structure and the endomembrane system maintain similarities across many different species.

Phylogenetic trees and cladograms are diagrams that show evolutionary relationships between organisms.

   • Phylogenies are based upon DNA, RNA, amino acid sequences or morphological data.
   • All phylogenies need to be rooted and a have a **common ancestor** to the organisms at that root.
   • The organisms with the *fewest number of differences* have shared a common ancestor most recently.
   • An **outgroup** can be used as a reference point. The outgroup will have all shared traits and derived traits will be more evident.
   • A **node** represents a hypothetical ancestor and includes the common ancestor plus all of the descendents. It is signified by a **O** where two lines meet.
   • **Bars** are located between **clades** and are labeled with a new trait that prior organisms did not have.

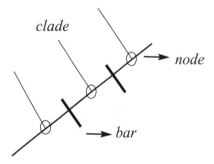

There is a diverse array of modern organisms. All of these organisms evolved from a common ancestor through similar evolutionary processes.

Domain Name	Features of Domain Members
Domain Bacteria	Prokaryotic cells, diverse life modes (can be nitrogen-fixing, photosynthetic, parasitic), often have cell walls of peptidoglycan, most use oxygen gas for cellular respiration, can be autotrophic or heterotrophic, unicellular, often have flagella
Domain Archae	Prokaryotic cells, live in extreme environments like salt marshes and deep sea vents, often live in anaerobic conditions, unicellular
Domain Eukarya	Eukaryotic cells, includes unicellular and multicellular forms, includes autotrophs and heterotrophs, includes four major kingdoms of organisms (Protista, Plantae, Animalia, Fungi)

Four Kingdoms of Domain Eukarya

Kingdom Name	Features of Kingdom Members
Protista	Mostly unicellular, can be autotrophic or heterotrophic, complex organelle structure, can be free-living or parasitic, can have flagella or cilia
Plantae	Multicellular, terrestrial, autotrophic, cell walls of cellulose, chlorophyll a as the primary photosynthetic pigment, alternating life cycle
Fungi	Mostly multicellular, heterotrophic, cell walls of chitin, decomposers, mycelia form following plasmogamy, haploid life cycle
Animalia	Multicellular, motile, no cell walls, heterotrophic, most reproduce sexually, diploid life cycle

Similarities in animal features provide for variation among species and similarities within phyla.

Feature	Feature Description and Variations
Symmetry	Radial symmetry is when an organism can be divided into equal halves at multiple locations, bilateral symmetry occurs when organisms can only be cut at exactly one location to form equal halves
Tissues	Parazoa lack true tissues, eumatazoa have cells organized into tissue layers, diploblastic animals have only two tissue layers (endoderm and ectoderm) during development, triploblastic animals have endoderm, ectoderm, and mesoderm
Body Cavity	Acoelomates lack a body cavity between the three developmental layers, pseudocoelomates have a body cavity between the mesoderm and endoderm, coelomates have a body cavity completely lined with mesoderm tissue
Developmental Path	In protostome development, the blastopore becomes the mouth and cleavage is spiral; in deuterostomes, the blastopore becomes the anus and the cleavage is radial

Can you:

☐ determine relative relatedness between organisms as represented by a cladogram?

☐ draw a cladogram, if given names of organisms/groups and specific characteristics?

☐ identify and explain some typical bars derived or lost due to evolution (i.e. legs, vertebrae, heart chambers, hair, lungs, etc.)

☐ use data provided to determine what organisms shared a more common ancestor?

☐ discuss specific cellular similarities between related eukaryotes?

1.C Life continues to evolve within a changing environment.

• **Speciation and extinction have occurred throughout the Earth's history.**

• **Speciation may occur when two populations become reproductively isolated from each other.**

• **Populations of organisms continue to evolve.**

Speciation occurs when populations accumulate enough changes over time to lead to the emergence of a new species.

- **Speciation** requires that the beginning population become reproductively isolated.
    - Pre-zygotic isolating mechanisms prevent the sperm and egg from coming together.
    - Post-zygotic isolating mechanisms allow for a zygote to form, but not a healthy reproductive offspring.

P R E Z Y G O T I C	**Sexual isolation**	There is no attraction between the sexes of different species.
	Geographic isolation	The populations occur in different habitats within the same general area.
	Ecological isolation	Species utilize different resources within the ecosystem.
	Behavioral isolation	Species have different mating rituals.
	Temporal isolation	Mating or flowering occurs during different times or seasons.
	Mechanical isolation	Physical genitalia presents incompatibilities.
P O S T Z Y G O T I C	**Hybrid sterility**	The hybrids fail to produce functional gametes.
	Hybrid inviability	The hybrids have reduced viability or do not survive.
	Zygote mortality	Hybrid embryos do not develop properly.

- **Allopatric speciation** occurs when there is a geographic barrier that isolates the population.
- **Sympatric speciation** occurs without separation by a geographic barrier.
  - Polyploidy can lead to a new species in plants.
  - Food preference within a population range can lead to divergence.
  - Asynchronous mating times can lead to speciation.

Extinction occurs when a particular species encounters a tremendous amount of stress.

- Human impact (including hunting, trapping, overharvesting, introduced species, habitat destruction, pollution) can cause extinction.
- Natural causes (including climatic heating and cooling, changes in sea levels or currents, disease) can cause extinction.

Can you:

- ☐ explain the difference between allopatric and sympatric speciation?

- ☐ discuss how polyploidy can lead to a new species in plants?

- ☐ explain how a particular type of stress can cause extinction of a species?

- ☐ differentiate between prezygotic and postzygotic mechanisms of reproductive isolation?

- ☐ correctly use the terms hybrid, viability, sterility, and fertility when explaining postzygotic mechanisms of isolation?

1. D The origin of living systems is explained by natural processes.

- **There are several hypotheses about the natural origin of life on Earth, each with supporting scientific evidence.**
- **Scientific evidence from many different disciplines supports models of the origin of life.**

Biological Classification provides a means of grouping organisms that share physiological and structural similarities. This evidence helps to develop hypotheses about evolutionary relationships.

- These differences were so great that it warranted the separation of that one kingdom into two different domains: Bacteria and Archae. Members of all other kingdoms have more molecular similarities than members of these two **domains**, so, all other kingdoms were placed into a common domain: Eukarya
- Modern Classification System from most inclusive to most exclusive.

  - ✓ Domain
  - ✓ Kingdom
  - ✓ Phylum
  - ✓ Class
  - ✓ Order
  - ✓ Family
  - ✓ Genus
  - ✓ Species

- The **domain** was added because in previous systems, all prokaryotic organisms were placed together in one Kingdom. With advances in molecular techniques, it was found that true bacteria and Archae are very diverse.

The first living cell evolved nearly four billion years ago through a process of chemical evolution or abiotic synthesis.

- The early earth had a very volatile atmosphere with many small inorganic gases like H_2O, CO, CO_2, CH_4, N_2, and H_2. There wasn't any oxygen gas in the early earth's atmosphere.
- With the early earth's pressures and the extreme amounts of energy due to lightning, UV rays, volcanic activity, small inorganic molecules could have formed organic **monomers.**
- Miller and Urey showed that **amino acids** could be formed from the small inorganic molecules in the atmosphere with the right conditions.
- Panspermia hypothesis says that organic monomers could have been introduced on a meteor from space.
- Small organic monomers with negative charges bound to clay and iron pyrite particles. The excess energy would link the monomers and build the first organic **polymers**.

- The earth's volatile conditions would force proteins inside a lipid bubble and form the first **protobionts**.
- RNA would get trapped inside a **protobiont** to form the first living cell (RNA hypothesis).
- The first living cell would have a simple lipid membrane, proteins, RNA as the genetic material, and be **unicellular, heterotrophic** and **prokaryotic**.
- **Autotrophs** would cause for the production of oxygen gas and the introduction of oxygen gas in the atmosphere 2 billion years ago

The theory of serial endosymbiosis explains the evolution of eukaryotic cells from the prokaryotic ancestors.

- Two prokaryotic cells began as **symbionts**.
- A smaller prokaryotic cell was engulfed by a larger prokaryotic cell.
- Each cell gained a benefit from the association; perhaps smaller one was protected from environment and perhaps the larger one gained some nutrient support.
- Over time, the two would become one cell; the smaller one becoming a mitochondrion if it was **heterotrophic** and a chloroplast if it was autotrophic.
- Both mitochondria and chloroplasts have their own DNA and ribosomes. The membranes of mitochondria and chloroplasts are more like the membrane of a prokaryote.

Can you:

☐ explain the theory of serial endosymbiosis?

☐ correctly identify potential heterotrophic and autotrophic eukaryotic ancestors?

☐ identify and justify characteristics of the first living cell?

☐ use proper taxonomy when describing relatedness of organisms within phylogenetic trees and cladograms?

☐ discuss similarities and differences between the three Domains in order to justify relatedness between organisms?

Multiple-Choice Questions

Each of the following questions is followed by four possible answers. Select the best answer for each question.

1. Scientists have discovered differences in the stream communities of guppy populations in Caribbean islands. Upstream, there are fewer predators of the guppies, whereas downstream, predators thrive. Which of the following scenarios is most likely as an evolutionary effect of this ecological difference?

    (A) Guppies found upstream will grow more quickly, stay small in size and reproduce early in life.
    (B) Guppies in the high predation pools will exhibit drab coloration.
    (C) Guppies found downstream reproduce slowly and die older.
    (D) The guppy populations downstream will be larger.

2. A population of budgies has 37 individuals who are blue in color and 194 individuals who express the dominant green color. What is the dominant allele frequency for this population? Answer: _____

	Percentage of Single Gene Mutations in Specific Populations		
	African Americans	**European Americans**	**Asian Americans**
Cystic Fibrosis	21%	71%	8%
Phenylketonuria	4%	82%	14%
Sickle Cell Anemia	98%	<1%	<1%

3. The chart above shows the percentage of single gene disorders in specific American populations. Which of the following is **NOT** a plausible explanation for the variance in the data as described above?

    (A) The disease frequency varies from year to year in specific populations.
    (B) Disease frequency among different populations results from genetic differences as well as environmental differences.
    (C) Some genetic variations associated with disease may prevail in specific populations because they provide a selective advantage to some populations.
    (D) A small population of individuals with a defective gene has grown, and the gene has increased in frequency because it has not interfered with reproductive fitness.

Human beta chain	0
Gorilla	1
Gibbon	2
Rhesus monkey	8
Dog	15
Horse, cow	25
Mouse	27
Gray kangaroo	38
Chicken	45
Frog	67
Lamprey	125
Sea slug	127
Soybean	124

4. In the chart, the numbers represent the number of amino acid differences between the beta chain of humans and the hemoglobins of the other species. Which of the following statements is supported by the data?

(A) The cow is more closely related to the dog than the mouse.
(B) The kangaroo diverged from a common ancestor more recently than the gorilla.
(C) A gray kangaroo and chicken are more closely related than a rhesus monkey and a dog.
(D) Humans are more closely related to a jawless fish than to a mollusk.

5. In a particular species of insects, you observe that over the last 300 years, the color pattern has alternated from being overwhelmingly blue with a few orange and red forms to the current pattern where the orange and red forms are dominant and there are only a few blue specimens. What type of natural selection may lead to this observation?

(A) Stabilizing selection
(B) Disruptive selection
(C) Diversifying selection
(D) Directional selection

6. A natural disaster devastates an area of the midwestern United States, causing mass extinction of several species. Which of the following scenarios is LEAST likely to occur in the years following the devastation?

   (A) The remaining organisms may quickly diversify and begin establishing themselves in the new ecosystem.
   (B) The species will repopulate in the same manner as prior to the natural disaster.
   (C) Post extinction species may fail to diversify due to the changes in the ecosystem that are not suited to their survival.
   (D) The genetic diversity of the population will decrease, as a bottleneck was incurred.

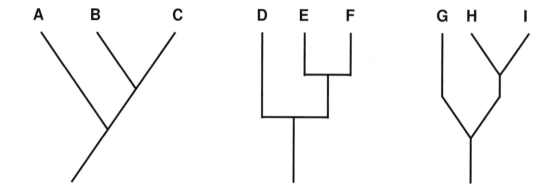

7. Which of the following statements is true regarding the cladograms above, all of which show the relatedness between species (A-I)?

   (A) The cladograms would explain the same relationships if G and H were reversed on the second cladograms.
   (B) Assuming the three letters in each cladograms represent earthworms, lizards and crocodiles, earthworms could not represent letters E, C, or H.
   (C) Species H and I are more closely related than Species B and C.
   (D) Species D is more distantly related to Species F than to Species E.

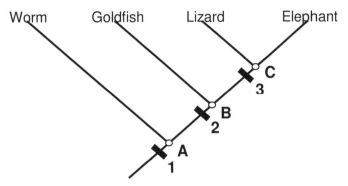

8. Cladograms are constructed based upon shared characteristics of organisms and show relatedness of those organisms. Which of the following statements about the clades is correct?

   (A) Bar 1 represents the presence of a backbone.
   (B) Node B represents invertebrates.
   (C) Bar 2 represents the presence of a backbone.
   (D) Node C represents mammals.

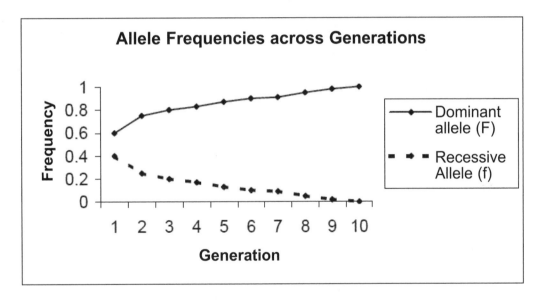

9. Which of the following statements is supported by the graph?

   (A) The population is in Hardy Weinberg equilibrium, as the sum of the frequency of the dominant allele and the recessive allele is always equal to 1.
   (B) The percentage of individuals homozygote recessive for this particular trait is increasing over time.
   (C) Selection has caused frequencies to change over time because individuals with a dominant allele survive at higher rates than individuals with recessive alleles.
   (D) Individuals who are homozygous recessive for this particular trait have migrated into the population, causing the frequency to approach 1.

10. Which of the following species will cause evolution to occur?

    (A) A species of salmon found in Japan is determined to be infertile due to an acid release from a hydroelectric dam in to the river where the salmon live.
    (B) There is a wide range of colors and banding patterns in a species of tropical air breathing tree snails on the island of O'ahu.
    (C) There is substantial food in a given Midwestern ecosystem for several species of squirrels, rabbits, and small rodents throughout the fall season.
    (D) Males and females within a species of *Drosophila* appear to mate randomly through several generations.

11. Which of the following is not a substantial form of evidence for the theory of evolution by natural selection?

    (A) The bones in a bat's wing and a horse's leg are structurally similar, however they do not provide the same function.
    (B) Cats and whales contain the same structural genes for formation of undifferentiated limbs.
    (C) The borders of Australia are indicative of the limits of the distribution of marsupial mammals, such as the kangaroo.
    (D) Off of Ecuador, identical species of tortoises, and differing food sources, are found on each of the Galapagos islands

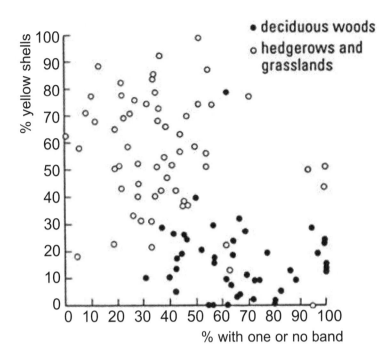

12. The graph above shows the distribution of snail shells that were collected in the spring of a given year. Which of the following can be concluded from this distribution?

   (A) The distribution of snails will remain constant even if humans were to clear the woodlands.
   (B) As thrush (a key predator of snails) populations diminish, the beneficial effects of camouflage for the snails will increase.
   (C) If the amount of woodlands decreases, the number of yellow snails will increase.
   (D) Yellow shelled snails are more common in the deciduous woods.

13. Which of the following scenarios does NOT promote substantial variation within a population?

   (A) During metaphase of meiosis I, crossing over occurs between homologous chromosomes.
   (B) A mutation occurs in the DNA sequence of an organism.
   (C) Alleles of different genes assort independently of one another during metaphase I of meiosis.
   (D) Two related organisms of the same species from an extremely small gene pool mate with one another.

14. A particular virus that affects the white blood cells of cats occurs in the large domesticated population at a rate of approximately 1-5%, whereas the disease rate in the reduced cheetahs is nearly 60%. Which of the following explains the difference in disease rate in these two populations?

    (A) The gene pool of the cheetah is extremely small, therefore the DNA is very similar throughout the population.
    (B) The increased genetic diversity of the cheetah population makes it more susceptible to the virus.
    (C) Cheetahs drive off their young after birth to avoid interbreeding.
    (D) Domesticated cats are administered a highly ineffective vaccine against the virus.

15. Natural selection works in many ways in various populations. Which of the following does not show selection to work in a directional sense?

    (A) Bees visit plants with larger petals more frequently.
    (B) Peahens preferentially mate with peacocks who have large, symmetrical fans.
    (C) Female birds select their mate based upon the complexity and beauty of a male designed nest.
    (D) Humans select mates without knowledge of their blood types.

16. Which of the following does not support the theory of serial endosymbiosis?

    (A) Both mitochondria and chloroplasts contain DNA different from the nucleus and similar to that of bacteria.
    (B) Mitochondria and chloroplasts are synthesized through a process quite similar to binary fission.
    (C) Mitochondria and chloroplasts contain double cell membranes.
    (D) Mitochondria and chloroplasts do not contain ribosomes, which is similar to bacterial structure.

17. Which of the following is an example of convergent evolution?

   (A) The kit fox lives in the desert and its coat helps it to disguise it from its predators. The red fox lives in the forest, where the red coat helps to camouflage the fox. In the desert, the ears of the kit fox have evolved to efficiently remove excess body heat.

   (B) A group of birds migrating end up in a new environment due to abnormal winds. If the food source is such that a particular beak is an advantage to survival, then this trait will increase in the population. In the birds' former location, perhaps this beak is not advantageous, and the beak traits will have a different frequency in that population.

   (C) The eyes of squid and octopus are strikingly similar to those of mammals, although both groups evolved entirely separately from one another.

   (D) Apple maggot flies once infested hawthorns. However, some flies began to infest apples and reproduced very quickly due to the abundant food source. Two species evolved, one that infests the native hawthorn and one that reproduces when apples are ripe.

18. Northern elephant seals were hunted by humans in the 1890s and their population was reduced to approximately 20 individuals. Which of the following is true about this population?

   (A) The population of seals will be more able to adapt to new pressures, such as a change in climate.

   (B) They have greater genetic variation than a population of southern elephant seals who were not hunted.

   (C) The northern seals will be less susceptible to disease and pollution than the southern elephant seals.

   (D) As the gene pool decreases, the chance of inbreeding will increase within the population of seals.

19. Organisms are classified by scientist based upon the relationships between those organisms. In which domain would you place a photosynthetic, prokaryotic organism with no membrane bound organelles, lacking peptidogylcan in its cell wall?

   (A) Eukarya
   (B) Monera
   (C) Eubacteria
   (D) Archaebacteria

20. Which of the following explains relationships between the current three Domain system?

(A) Archae have some histone like proteins that form a complex with DNA which is similar to organisms in Eukarya.
(B) Organisms in both Eubacteria and Eukarya contain membrane bound organelles and nuclei.
(C) Organisms in all three of the Domains contain cell walls made up of the same substance.
(D) Archaebacteria contain mitochondria which makes them closely related to photosynthetic eukaryotes.

21. Which of the following has a greater effect in small populations?

(A) Probability that a new mutation will be effectively neutral
(B) New mutations per year in the whole population
(C) New mutations per generation in the whole population
(D) Neutral mutation rate per individual

22. Often, new plant and animal species begin to inhabit new, remote islands located off of the mainland. This is an extremely random process. Which of the following species is least likely to colonize remote islands?

(A) Egg laying terrestrial mammals
(B) Birds, bats, flying insects, and seeds that use wind dispersal
(C) Small lizards and insects that can survive without water
(D) Rats, fruits and vegetables that travel with humans

23. As new islands are colonized, which of the following is **LEAST** likely to happen?

(A) If the island is completely isolated, the new island population will diverge quickly resulting in endemic species.
(B) Disease will be less likely to impact the endemic species due to the small size of the population.
(C) Endemic species will become less likely to survive if other species colonize the island.
(D) If the island is close, more species will migrate to the island, reducing the effects of genetic drift.

Year									
2002		**2003**		**2004**		**2005**		**2006**	
Ciprofloxacin	Penicillin	Ciprofloxacin	Penicillin	Ciprofloxacin	Penicillin	Ciprofloxacin	Penicillin	Ciprofloxacin	Penicillin
% of population displaying resistance 1.6	0.9	1.9	1.0	4.6	1.1	6.5	4.7	9.4	8.6

24. In California, between the years 2002-2006, the antibiotic resistance of bacteria was measured when treated with two different classes of antibiotics. Which of the following explanations is appropriate for the data indicated above?

    (A) The bacteria have learned to avoid the *Ciprofloxacin* but not the *Penicillin*.
    (B) The bacteria are trying to adapt to the antibiotics and are more successful against the *Ciprofloxacin*.
    (C) Neither *Ciprofloxacin* or *Penicillin* are effective against the bacteria.
    (D) The bacteria developed resistance more quickly to the *Ciprofloxacin*, however, also developed resistance to *Penicillin* at the end of the study.

25. In the late 1400s, Columbus brought small, hot peppers to Europe. The bell peppers that we eat now are larger and sweeter, and have a thicker flesh, than any of the original peppers. How did this change ultimately occur in peppers over time?

    (A) Europeans ate the smallest peppers from each crop and planted the seeds from the remaining peppers as the next crop.
    (B) Columbus' peppers were genetically very similar to current bell peppers and larger peppers occurred randomly.
    (C) Europeans chose the seeds from the smaller peppers for the next season's crop, so the only peppers left to eat were the large peppers.
    (D) Mutations in the genes coding for shape and size occurred over time, producing extra large peppers.

26. A tigon forms from a mating between a male tiger and a lioness. A tigon has a standard body size and life expectancy. Although it is possible for a tigon to be fertile, they are generally sterile. The type of isolating mechanism present between the tigers and the lions is

    (A) gametic mortality
    (B) temporal isolation
    (C) habitat isolation
    (D) hybrid sterility

27. One hundred fifty years ago, there were many white and gray rats that ran through the streets of London. Now, there are only gray rats in London remaining. Which description best explains the white rats in London?

   (A) The heterozygous genotype has increased in frequency through stabilizing selection.
   (B) The white color trait has disappeared due to directional selection.
   (C) The white fur color will increase in frequency over the next fifty years.
   (D) The gray color has replaced the white color as the dominant phenotype through mutation.

28. Life evolved on earth between 3.5 and 4 billion years ago. All of the following statements are probably true about that first living organism except for

   (A) it would have a singular chromosome of DNA like most bacteria
   (B) it would have a simple lipid cell membrane
   (C) it would be prokaryotic and unicellular
   (D) proteins, lipids, and nucleic acids would each be present in the first organism.

29. Rotifers are small, microscopic animals that live in freshwater. They can reproduce sexually like all animals. However, most often, they reproduce through the asexual mechanism of parthenogenesis. How would the frequency of parthenogenesis affect the evolution of rotifers?

   (A) Haploid females will show more signs of sexual dimorphisms.
   (B) All offspring would be genetic clones of the parent organism.
   (C) Having all of the genetic information from one parent would limit the amount of genetic variation in the population over time.
   (D) Through sexual selection, there would be more males than females in the population.

Year	Frequency of Tongue Rolling	Frequency of Inability to roll tongue
1925	65%	35%
1950	68%	32%
1975	66%	34%
2000	67%	33%

30. Tongue rolling in humans is due to a dominant allele that is inherited through simple dominance and recessiveness. The frequencies of the tongue-rolling trait from 1925 to 2000 are shown in the table. Why has the frequency of this trait remained fairly constant in the human population?

   (A) Since humans have been able to manipulate the environment, they are not affect by simple selection pressures.
   (B) Tongue-rolling has provided a reproductive advantage and has increased reproductive fitness in humans.
   (C) Tongue-rolling is neutral variation that does not provide any selective advantage in the human population.
   (D) The frequency of tongue-rolling is linked to another trait that yields a reproductive advantage.

Free-Response Questions for Big Idea #1

Directions: On the AP biology exam, there will be 8 free-response questions. They will have a variety of lengths and be worth a variety of points. Longer essays are worth up to 10 points. Short essays of 2, 3, 4 or 6 points are possible as well. For these questions, follow the given instructions. Write clear complete responses in complete sentences for each question. Grading rubrics for these practice free-response questions are provided in the teacher's manual that accompanies this review book.

1. **10 points are possible on this question.**

The frequency of the sickle cell disease in parts of Central Africa is as high as 10% compared to a frequency of .5% in the United States.

   a. Why are the frequencies of these traits different in these two areas? Explain why and how these differences are possible.
   b. Use the percentage for the western Africa population and the US population to calculate the frequency of the heterozygous and homozygous dominant genotypes in each of these areas.
   c. Is there evidence of heterozygote advantage in either one of these populations? Explain the evidence of lack or evidence.

2. **4 points are possible on this question.**

A population of crickets feeds on two species of weedy plant (A and B). Both plants are spread across the habitat range of this population. There aren't any physical barriers to prevent crickets from moving between the plants. After many generations, the crickets that were born on plant A have begun to only eat plant A and mate with other plant A crickets. The crickets born on plant B have begun to eat only plant B and mate with only plant B crickets.

   a. Is there evidence for speciation in this population? Explain the evidence.
   b. Is this an example of sympatric or allopatric speciation? Explain your response. What kinds of isolating mechanisms are present in this population?

3. **4 points are possible on this question.**

Natural selection is the major mechanism for evolution as described in the Origin of Species by Charles Darwin.

    a. Explain evolution by natural selection.
    b. Use one of the following examples to explain the process of natural selection.

        i. Finches on the Galapagos Islands
        ii. Armadillos and giant armadillo-like mammals
        iii. Standard sloths and extinct giant sloths
        iv. Horses and zebras

4. **2 points are possible.**

One theory for the evolution of the first organic macromolecules like proteins, carbohydrates, and lipids is called chemical evolution. In this theory, explain how the small inorganic molecules in the atmosphere could lead to organic macromolecules.

5. **10 points are possible.**

The most supported theory about how the first eukaryotic cells evolved from prokaryotic ancestors is through a process called serial endosymbiosis.

    a. Explain the process of serial endosymbiosis.
    b. Explain the evidence for serial endosymbiosis.
    c. There are three domains of life. Draw a phylogeny that shows the evolutionary relationships of these three organisms.
    d. Explain the phylogeny and the common ancestor of these three domains.

NO TESTING MATERIAL PRINTED ON THIS PAGE

GO ON TO THE NEXT PAGE

BIG IDEA!

Big Idea #2: Biological systems utilize energy and molecular building blocks to grow, to reproduce, and to maintain homeostasis

Key Terms for this section:

- abiotic
- active transport
- adaptive radiation
- anabolic reactions
- apomixis
- asexual reproduction
- ATP
- ATP synthetase
- binary fission
- biotic
- budding
- Calvin cycle
- catabolic reactions
- chemiosmosis
- chloroplast
- community
- competitive inhibitor
- concentration gradient
- consumers
- cooperativity
- courtship behavior
- cryptic coloration
- cuticle
- cyclic photophosphorylation
- cytoskeleton
- diffusion

- divergent evolution
- ecosystem
- endergonic reactions
- energy coupling
- enthalpy
- entropy
- exergonic reactions
- facilitated diffusion
- feedback inhibition
- fermentation
- G proteins
- glycolysis
- Golgi apparatus
- homeostasis
- hypertonic
- hypotonic
- isotonic
- Krebs cycle
- lysosome
- metabolism
- meiosis
- mitochondrion
- mitosis
- negative feedback
- net primary productivity
- noncyclic photophosphorylation

- nucleus
- osmoconformer
- osmoregulator
- osmosis
- passive transport
- periodic disturbances
- pheromones
- photosynthesis
- phylogeny
- population
- positive feedback
- primary succession
- producers
- regeneration
- ribosome
- rough endoplasmic reticulum
- rubisco
- secondary succession
- sexual reproduction
- sexual selection
- smooth endoplasmic reticulum
- speciation
- transcription factors
- trophic levels
- vegetative reproduction

29

2.A: Growth, reproduction and maintenance of the organization of living systems require free energy and matter.

- **All living systems (organisms, populations, ecosystems) require constant input of free energy.**
- **Organisms capture and store free energy for use in highly evolved biological processes.**
- **An exchange of matter is crucial within environments for growth, reproduction and to maintain organization.**

Energy moves through all biological organisms and systems

- Cells use chemical energy in the form of organic molecules. Chemical bonds can be broken to release chemical energy.
- **Catabolic reactions** break down large molecules into smaller ones. These reactions release energy.
- **Anabolic reactions** build large molecules from smaller components. These reactions consume energy.
- Cells utilize cellular energy in the form of **ATP** or some other chemical carrier. These molecules have a structure that is easy to form and easy to break to access the stored energy.

Energy input into a system must be constant and greater than energy lost.

- The amount of free energy lost as heat to the environment is called entropy. The amount of entropy in the universe is always increasing.
- **Energy coupling** occurs when the energy from a catabolic reaction is stored in ATP so that it can be available to an anabolic reaction.
- Some cells use energy from sunlight for biological processes.
- Energy is always transferred. Some transfer mechanisms are more efficient than others. However, no energy transfers are 100% efficient. \

The properties of water impact living systems.

- **Polarity** – water is a polar molecule, with a partial positive charge at one end and a negative charge at the other end.
- **Hydrogen bonding** – bonds between these partial positive and partial negative charges are hydrogen bonds. Hydrogen bonds are transient (short lived), however are very numerous in solution.

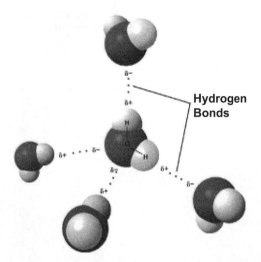

- **Adhesion** – the attraction of a water molecule to another substance
- **Cohesion** – the attraction of one water molecule to another water molecule
- **High specific heat capacity** – due to cohesion, water molecules resist increasing their motion and rapid changes in temperature
- **Universal solvent** – water is a hydrophilic solvent and therefore dissolves most substances.
  - **solute** – a substance that is dissolved
  - **solvent** – the substance that does the dissolving
  - **solution** – the solvent and the solute dissolved together
- **Heat of vaporization** – it takes a lot of heat to evaporate water due to the frequent breaking and reforming of hydrogen bonds

Organisms obtain nutrients and eliminate waste products efficiently by maintaining high surface area to volume ratios at the cellular level.

- It is not advantageous for cells to be extremely large. As the volume of a cell increases, the surface area decreases while there is an increased need for resources. Therefore, there is a limitation on cell size.

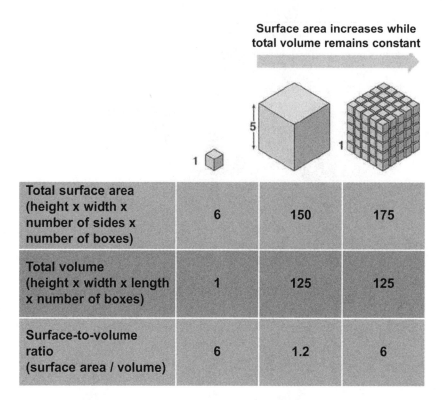

Total surface area (height x width x number of sides x number of boxes)	6	150	175
Total volume (height x width x length x number of boxes)	1	125	125
Surface-to-volume ratio (surface area / volume)	6	1.2	6

Specific cellular structures are used to maximize the exchange of materials with the environment. Some examples of these structures are:

- ○ **Root hairs** are thin extensions of the root that increase surface area for water/mineral absorption.
- ○ **Alveoli** are thin, small sacs in the lungs to increase surface area and maximize gas exchange.
- ○ **Villi** and **microvilli** are finger like projections of the small intestine to increase surface are to increase absorption.

Organisms use various metabolic and reproductive strategies to maximize free energy changes and minimize disruptions to the population size and to the ecosystem.

- **Ectothermic animals**—allow the cellular environment of the organisms to fluctuate with the environment
- **Endothermic animals**—maintain a cellular environment that is different from the environment; requires higher metabolic rate.

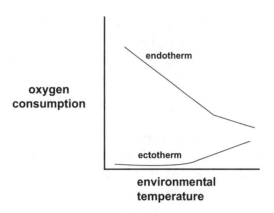

- Most plants and animals do not reproduce year round. Instead, they reproduce seasonally, in some instances driven by the following biotic and abiotic factors:
  - Peak periods of predation on eggs
  - Availability of nesting locations
  - Humidity and soil moistness
  - Temperature
- Based on its life cycle, a plant is classified as an **annual, biennial**, or **perennial**.
  - **Annual** – germination, flowering and death all occur within one growing season
  - **Biennial** – the entire life cycle takes two years; first year includes growth of leaves, stems and roots and the second year includes growth of the flower
  - **Perennial** – grow and bloom every year; require specialized structures for reproduction and dormancy
- Smaller animals tend to have higher metabolic rates
- If the number of producers changes in an ecosystem, the number and size of other trophic levels will be affected.

Organisms use different mechanisms to capture and store free energy.

- **Autotrophs** capture free energy from the environment.
  - **Photosynthetic** organisms use the sun as a source of energy.
  - **Chemosynthetic** organisms use inorganic molecules as a source of energy.
- **Heterotrophs** capture free energy by consuming other organisms.

Fermentation, cellular respiration, and photosynthesis are biological processes that involve coordinated energy transformations and different electron acceptors.

Anaerobic respiration:

- occurs when oxygen is unavailable to cells
- contains two stages, glycolysis and fermentation (either alcohol or lactic acid)oxygen is NOT the final electron acceptor in anaerobic respiration
- ATP yield is greatly reduced as compared to aerobic respiration
- two stages: glycolysis and alcohol fermentation or lactic acid fermentation

- ○ **Glycolysis** is the breakdown of glucose. It occurs in the cytosol. The glucose sugar goes through some chemical alterations and yields 2 pyruvate molecules. In the process, 2 ATP molecules are harvested and 2 NADH molecules. The pyruvate is the carbon compound with the potential energy. The ATP and NADH are molecules that act as cellular energy.
- ○ **Alcohol fermentation** occurs in the cytosol. It follows glycolysis when oxygen is NOT present in plants, fungi and bacteria. The pyruvate molecules are converted to ethanol. NADH is converted back to NAD+ for additional glucose breakdown to yield ATP.
- ○ **Lactic acid fermentation** occurs in the cytosol. It follows glycolysis when oxygen is NOT present in animals. The pyruvate molecules are converted to lactic acid NADH is converted back to NAD+ for additional glucose breakdown to yield ATP.

Aerobic respiration:

- occurs in cells to produce cellular energy when oxygen is present
- most stages occur inside the mitochondrion
- occurs in all organisms that have mitochondria
- most efficient transfer of the potential energy in glucose to cellular energy in the form of ATP
- four stages: glycolysis, pyruvate oxidation, Krebs cycle, and oxidative phosphorylation
    - ○ **Glycolysis** begins with glucose. It occurs in the cytosol. The glucose sugar goes through some chemical alterations and yields 2 pyruvate molecules. In the process, 2 ATP molecules are harvested and 2 NADH molecules. The pyruvate is the carbon compound with the potential energy. The ATP and NADH are molecules that act as cellular energy.
    - ○ **Pyruvate oxidation** occurs in the mitochondrial matrix. The oxidation of the pyruvates produces 2 NADH molecules and 2 Acetyl CoA which are the starting molecule for the Krebs cycle.
    - ○ The **Krebs cycle** occurs in the mitochondrial matrix. There are 2 cycles per glucose molecule. The energy from the sugar is harvested and stored as 10 NADH, 2 FADH2, and 2 ATP molecules. The NADH and the FADH2 are both converted to ATP in later reactions.
    - ○ **Oxidative phosphorylation** occurs in the inner membrane of the mitochondrion. The electrons from the NADH and FADH2 are harvested and past through a series of electronegative proteins to actively transport H+ ions to the intermembrane space to create a proton gradient. The H+ ions diffuse through an enzyme called **ATP synthetase** and drive the production of 34 ATP molecules. This production of ATP through the ATP synthetase enzyme due to a concentration gradient is called **chemiosmosis**.

Can you compare and contrast aerobic and anaerobic respiration?

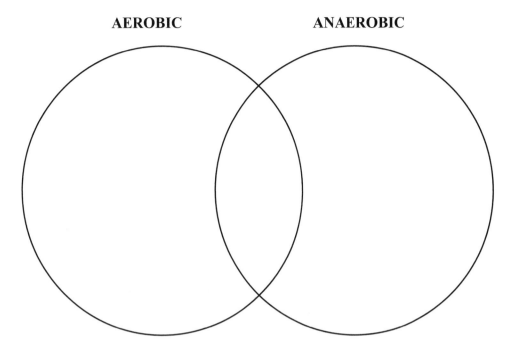

AEROBIC   ANAEROBIC

Photosynthesis:

- occurs where the energy from the sun is converted to chemical energy in the form of sugar
- occurs in autotrophs like plants, algae, and cyanobacteria
- occurs inside the chloroplast.
  - **Noncyclic photophosphorylation** occurs in the thylakoid membranes. It takes the energy from the sun and stores in ATP and NADPH. The ATP is made by chemiosmosis with ATP synthetase. Oxygen is produced in this process as electrons are pulled from a water molecule.
  - **Cyclic photophosphorylation** occurs in the thylakoid membranes. It takes the energy from the sun and stores in ATP only. The ATP is synthesized by chemiosmosis with ATP synthetase.
  - The **Calvin cycle** uses rubisco to bind carbon dioxide to the organic molecules in the process. It uses the energy from the ATP and NADPH from noncyclic and cyclic photophosphorylation to drive the process. Sugar is produced. One glucose molecule is produced from every 6 cycles of the Calvin-Benson cycle.

Can you:

☐ **describe** the way that energy moves through and is transformed in biological systems?

☐ **explain** how the amount of entropy in the universe increases?

☐ **identify** and **describe** the difference between catabolic reactions and anabolic reactions?

☐ **explain** the processes of anaerobic respiration, aerobic respiration, and photosynthesis?

☐ **identify** the electron acceptors in the different energy capturing processes?

☐ **compare** and **contrast** the processes of anaerobic and aerobic respiration?

☐ **explain** how the concentration gradient is created during chemiosmosis and **discuss** the risk-reward energy scenario for this process?

☐ **explain** how the structural features of cells allow organisms to capture, store or use free energy?

☐ **discuss** the different metabolic and reproductive strategies plants and animals use to maximize free energy (endothermic vs. exothermic, perennial vs. biennial vs. annual)?

☐ **identify** and **describe** the structure and function of specific ways animals maximize surface area to volume ratios?

☐ **discuss** how the properties of water affect living systems?

2.B: Growth, reproduction and dynamic homeostasis require that cells create and maintain internal environments that are different from their external environments.

- Cell membranes are selectively permeable due to their structure.
- Growth and dynamic homeostasis are maintained by constant movement of molecules across membranes.
- Eukaryotic cells maintain internal membranes that partition the cell into specialized regions.

The plasma membrane is a dynamic entity with a mosaic of different molecules present.

- The plasma membrane is composed of several different molecules. These molecules are not physically connected so the membrane is very fluid. The molecules can move around, but are positioned due to their chemical properties.
- There is a **phospholipid bilayer** present. The polar phosphate groups line up along the outside and the inside of the membrane structure. The nonpolar fatty acids are put in the middle of the membrane structure to avoid contact with the aqueous environment on the inside and the outside of the cell.
- There are large **integral proteins** that bridge both layers of the phospholipid bilayer. These proteins are amphipathic with the polar regions at the inside and outside of the membrane and the nonpolar regions in the middle. These proteins can be channels, pumps, membrane-bound enzymes, receptors, etc..
- There are smaller **peripheral proteins** that lie on the inside or the outside of the membrane bilayer, but because of their smaller size, they do not bridge both layers of the membrane. On the inside these proteins are often involved in relaying signals from a signal transduction pathway, like G proteins. On the outside, these proteins are often receptor proteins or proteins that have oligosaccharides attached.
- **Cholesterol** molecules are present along the nonpolar fatty acid area in the middle of the bilayer. These molecules help to maintain the membrane's fluidity by preventing membrane solidification.
- **Oligosaccharides** are short carbohydrate chains that are attached to the surface of a membrane-bound protein. These chains act as molecular identity tags for the cell.

Can you label the cell membrane?

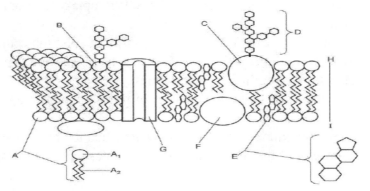

Plasma membranes are selectively permeable and cellular energy or concentration gradients can be used to drive transport.

- The plasma membrane is **selectively permeable** or **semipermeable**. It regulates what molecules move across the plasma membrane.
- Small, nonpolar or uncharged molecules can often move across the lipid bilayer of the plasma membrane. Large polar molecules and ions need embedded channel and transport proteins to aid the transport across the membrane.
- Molecules move from high concentration to low concentration through the process of **diffusion**.
- When ions or polar molecules move from high concentration to low, they pass through a membrane-bound integral protein in a process of **facilitated diffusion**.
- **Osmosis** involves the movement of water from high water concentration to low water concentration or from high water potential to low water potential
- **Aquaporins** are proteins in the plasma membrane that increase the rate of water transport across the membrane.
- When the water concentration is the same on both sides of a membrane, the two environments are **isotonic**.
- An environment is **hypotonic** when it has a higher water concentration or higher water potential and a lower solute concentration.
- An environment is **hypertonic** when it has a lower water concentration or lower water potential and a higher solute concentration.

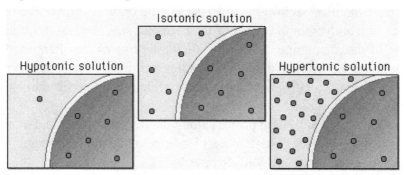

- **Active transport** uses the energy from ATP to move molecules from low concentration to high concentration. They move against the concentration gradient through a membrane-bound integral protein. Active transport requires membrane proteins.
- **Endocytosis** occurs when ATP is used for cells to uptake macromolecules and particulate matter.
  - **Phagocytosis** occurs when a large quantity of solid molecules is picked up. It is moved into the cell in a **vesicle**. Then, a **lysosome** digests the molecules with its hydrolytic enzymes.
  - **Pinocytosis** occurs when a quantity of fluids are picked up in a bulk manner across the membrane.
  - **Receptor-mediated endocytosis** occurs when the bulk molecule binds to a receptor of the cell. This binding initiates the endocytosis.

- **Exocytosis** occurs when molecules are moved in a bulk manner out of the cell. The molecules are sent through the Golgi complex to be wrapped by a membrane and sent across the plasma membrane.

Cell walls have a structural and functional purpose in the cell.

- Prokaryotes, fungi and plants have an external structural boundary called a **cell wall** to regulate passage of some substances to the cytoplasm.
- Plant cell walls are composed of **cellulose**, prokaryotic cell walls contain **peptidoglycan** and fungal cell walls are composed of **chitin** as primary components.

Eukaryotic cells have internal membranes that partition the cell.

- Prokaryotic cells (Archaea and Bacteria) **do not** have any structures in the endomembrane system.
- The **endomembrane system** consists of organelles that have a plasma membrane outside that is similar to the outside of the eukaryotic plasma membrane. These structures are found in **eukaryotes only**.
  - **Nucleus**—contains the chromosomes and the nucleus; it is surrounded by a double lipid bilayer called the nuclear envelope
  - **Rough endoplasmic reticulum**—next to nuclear envelope and made of lipid bilayer exterior; has attached ribosomes; site of membrane synthesis and protein folding
  - **Smooth endoplasmic reticulum**—lipid bilayer exterior; no attached ribosomes; site of phospholipid production and poison detoxification
  - **Golgi body/apparatus**—stack of lipid bilayer membranes; site of packaging of material to be sent from the cell and lysosome and vesicle maintenance
  - **Lysosome**—a small membrane pocket that holds hydrolytic enzymes; used in breakdown of nutrients and nonfunctional organelles
  - **Vesicle**—small piece of membrane that is used for temporary storage
  - **Vacuole**—membrane structure used for long-term storage

- These structures are not part of the endomembrane system and are not made from a eukaryotic lipid bilayer exterior.
  - **Mitochondrion**—double lipid bilayer structure; contains own DNA and ribosomes; site of cellular respiration
  - **Chloroplast**—double lipid bilayer structure; contains own DNA and ribosomes; site of photosynthesis
  - **Ribosome**—can be bound or free in eukaryotes; free in prokaryotes; two subunits; site of translation
  - **Flagella**—made from microtubules in eukaryotes; protein structures that whip back and forth for cellular movement
  - **Cilia**—microtubule structures found in animals and protists only; allow for cell movement or movement of materials along the surface
  - **Centriole**—found in animals only; helps to form the mitotic spindle apparatus in mitosis

Can you:

☐ **describe** the structure of the plasma membrane?

☐ **explain** how and why the plasma membrane is selectively permeable?

☐ **explain** how cellular energy or energy from concentration gradients drive molecular movement across membranes?

☐ **describe** the following transport processes: diffusion, passive transport, facilitated diffusion, osmosis, active transport, endocytosis, and exocytosis and **discuss** when and where they are present?

☐ **explain** the mechanisms and purposes of phagocytosis, pinocytosis, and receptor-mediated endocytosis?

☐ **explain** the structure and function of the eukaryotic endomembrane system?

☐ **discuss** cellular differences between prokaryotes and eukaryotes?

☐ **describe** the structure and function of the following organelles: nucleus, rough endoplasmic reticulum, smooth endoplasmic reticulum, Golgi mechanism, lysosome, vacuole, vesicle, mitochondrion, chloroplast, ribosome, flagella, centriole, and cilia?

2. C: Organisms use feedback mechanisms to regulate growth and reproduction, and to maintain dynamic homeostasis.

- Organisms use feedback mechanisms to maintain their internal environments and respond to external environmental changes.
- Organisms respond to changes in the external environments.

Organisms use specific feedback mechanisms to respond to environmental changes.

- **Homeostasis** is the maintenance of stable internal cellular conditions such as temperature, pH, salinity, ionic concentrations, etc. Aquatic and terrestrial animals maintain homeostasis in different ways.
  - ○ **Osmoconformers** are aquatic animals that allow their internal conditions to fluctuate with the environment
  - ○ **Osmoregulators** are aquatic animals that maintain internal cellular environments that are different from the outside environment; energy from metabolic activity is necessary to maintain these set environments

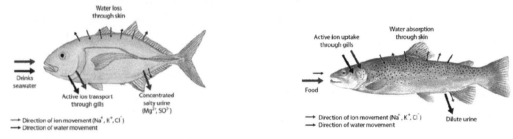

  - ○ **Ectothermic animals** allow the cellular environment of the organisms to fluctuate with the environment
  - ○ **Endothermic animals** maintain a cellular environment that is different from the environment; requires higher metabolic rate.

- **Positive feedback** is when the cellular processes increase the rate of a chemical reaction or cellular process and its occurrence further increases the rate. This often leads to a greater degree of instability
  - ○ **Labor onset during childbirth: Oxytocin** stimulates labor contractions. As the baby descends in the birth canal, pressure receptors in the uterus send messages to the brain to produce oxytocin. This causes the muscles in the uterine wall to contract. When the pressure receptors stop sending messages to the brain, the production of oxytocin stops and labor contractions cease.
  - ○ **Fruit ripening:** A ripe apple releases the hormone **ethylene** stimulating a variety of enzymes which convert starch and acids of the unripe fruit to sugars and softens the fruit by breaking down **pectins** in the cell wall. Exposure to ethylene stimulates the synthesis of more ethylene creating a positive feedback loop.

- **Negative feedback** is when a condition or chemical inhibits some cellular process and often maintains stability.
  - ○ **Insulin regulation:** When blood glucose levels increase, the pancreas releases insulin. Insulin increases glucose uptake in target cells and it is stored as glycogen. This decreases blood glucose levels, insulin secretion ceases, and glucose uptake mechanisms stop. However, when blood glucose levels decrease, **glucagon** is secreted to initiate the breakdown of glycogen to glucose in the liver and skeletal muscle cells until blood sugar levels reach a normal level.

When feedback systems are altered, these homeostatic mechanisms are often altered.

  - ○ **Response to dehydration:** When dehydration occurs, the blood contains less water and becomes more concentrated. As the blood becomes more concentrated, the hypothalamus triggers the release of **antidiuretic hormone (ADH)**. ADH increases the permeability of the distil tubule and collecting duct causing the urine to become more concentrated by allowing the reabsorption of more water. This dilutes the blood and therefore no ADH is released.

Organisms use cellular mechanisms to respond to environmental changes through behavioral and physiological mechanisms.

  - The effect of length of day and night on plant growth is called **photoperiodism**. Some plants require differing lengths of uninterrupted light and/or night.
  - The direction of plant growth is determined by the direction of the light source is called **phototropism**.

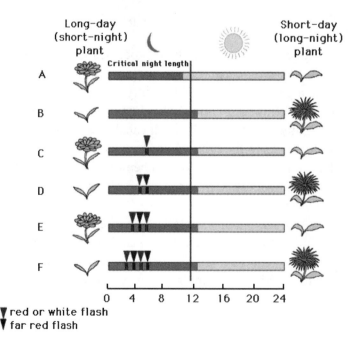

- **Kinesis** is a random turning or movement of an organism to a stimulus. **Taxis** involves an organism turning towards or away from a stimulus.
- **Chemotaxis** can be positive (towards a stimulus) or negative (away from a stimulus). **Somatic cells** (including neurons, lymphocytes, and sperm), bacteria and other multicellular organisms direct their movements according to certain chemicals in their environments. Chemotaxis is important for organisms to find food, avoid poisons, or for somatic cells to develop correctly (sperm towards egg, neuron or lymphocyte migration).
- Fungi reproduce sexually under unique conditions. **Meiosis** is the cellular mechanism behind sexual reproduction. Fungi are **haploid** for most of their life cycle, becoming **diploid** only for the purpose of meiosis, triggered by environmental cues.
- **Circadian rhythms** repeat once a day, persist without specific cues, can be adjusted to match local time differences and maintain the same clock regardless of temperature. **Biological clocks** are present in plants and animals. In mammals, the retina contains receptors that project to the hypothalamus to create a sleep-wake cycle. The **hypothalamus** sends a message to the pineal gland which causes increased **melatonin** secretion during the night and decreased secretion during the day.

Can you:

☐ **describe** homeostasis and **explain** how it is maintained?

☐ **explain** how positive and negative feedback systems function in organisms?

☐ **identify** and **discuss** at least one positive and negative feedback system in a specific organism?

☐ **explain** how photoperiodism is unique to specific types of plants?

☐ **compare** and **contrast** taxis and kinesis and design an experiment to test a hypothesis related to types of movement?

☐ **discuss** how fungi use meiosis in a unique way?

☐ **explain** how circadian rhythms function in mammals?

2. D: Growth and dynamic homeostasis of a biological system are influenced by changes in the system's environment.

- All biological systems from cells and organisms to populations, communities and ecosystems are affected by complex biotic and abiotic interactions involving exchange of matter and free energy.
- Homeostatic mechanisms reflect both common ancestry and divergence due to adaptation in different environments.
- Biological systems are affected by disruptions to their dynamic homeostasis.
- Plants and animals have a variety of chemical defenses against infections that affect dynamic homeostasis.

Community structure is affected by biotic and abiotic factors.

- **Abiotic factors** are non-living factors that affect communities. These features add energy and determine the format of the community and the changes to the community that occur in an area.
  - Temperature and climate
  - Periodic disturbances
  - Sunlight
  - Water availability
  - Rocks and soil
- **Biotic factors** are living components of the community that affect other organisms. Each organism affects the other organisms in the community through feeding and competition relationships.

Energy flows through trophic levels in the ecosystem.

- **Trophic levels**—feeding patterns in a community and the role that each population has in the energy transfer process
- **Food Chain**—simple graph of feeding structures where there is only one organism feeding on another
- **Food Web**—complex chain of feeding relationships in a community where organisms can feed on many different organisms in different trophic levels
- The first trophic level called the **producers** includes the autotrophs that can convert light energy to sugar in photosynthesis.
- The second trophic level called the **primary consumers** includes the herbivorous animals that eat the plants. Only 10% of the energy from the producers makes it to the primary consumers.
- The third trophic level called the **secondary consumers** includes carnivores that feed on the herbivores. Only 10% of the energy from the primary consumers goes to the secondary consumers.
- The fourth trophic level called the **tertiary consumers** feed on the secondary consumers. Only 10% of the energy from the secondary consumers is available to the tertiary consumers.

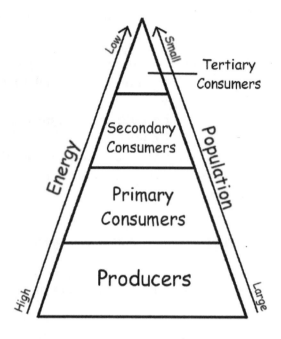

Ecosystems are always undergoing slow continuous change to structure and energy needs.

- Ecosystems are not static entities. They are very dynamic and undergo slow, gradual changes to their structure and energy demands; this process is called **ecological succession**.
- **Primary succession** occurs when a community begins to form in an area that is devoid of life or soil. It occurs as erosion breaks down rock surface. It often occurs following a volcanic eruption or an abandoned parking lot.
- **Secondary succession** occurs when change happens to an existing community or a new community grows where there is intact soil with seeds in the seed bank. It often follows fire, flood, tornadoes, earthquakes, etc.

Organisms have complex relationships and interactions in communities. These interactions are maintained by feeding and energy transfer patterns.

- When two species compete for a common resource, it is called **interspecific competition**. In this relationship, both species are negatively affected as they are forced to expend extra energy to compete for the limited resource.
- The **niche** is the ecological role of a population in the community structure.
- No two populations in a stable community can occupy the exact same niche. One population will always be a better competitor and will be successful in the environment. The poorer competing species will go extinct in the area. This phenomenon is known as the **competitive exclusion principle**.
- **Resource partitioning** can be used to allow different populations of animals to share a limited resource by utilizing that resource in a different way.
- In **commensalism**, one species benefits while the other is unaffected.

- In **mutualism**, both species in the relationship benefit.
- In **predation**, one species (the predator) benefits while the other species (the prey) is negatively affected.

Organisms have a variety of mechanisms to exchange nutrients and wastes with the environment.

- Aquatic and terrestrial plants exchange gas with the environment in unique ways.
  - In terrestrial plants, gas exchange occurs through pores called **stomata** in the **epidermis** of the leaf. The stomata are surrounded by **guard cells** that regulate the opening and closing of the stomata. In totally submerged aquatic plants, nutrients and dissolved gases diffuse through the epidermal cells which do not contain any cuticle. In plants that float above water, stomata may be located on the surface of the leaf, instead of the underside, to maximize gas exchange.

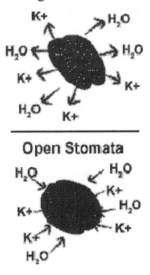

- Animals use unique digestive systems.
  - **Food vacuole:** Food vacuoles are storage sites for food taken in by the cell. **Lysosomes** fuse with food vacuoles and breakdown the macromolecules inside the vacuole.
  - **Gastrovascular cavities:** Digestion can occur in a gastrovascular cavity, which is a saclike body composed of two cell layers. The cavity has one opening that functions as a **mouth** and an **anus**. Within the cavity, extracellular digestion takes place.
  - **One way digestive systems:** Organisms with a one way digestive system possess two openings, a mouth and an anus. This **alimentary canal** may contain a **stomach**, or some site for mechanical and chemical breakdown of nutrients and an **intestine**, or a site for nutrient absorption.
- Aquatic and terrestrial animals use specific exchange mechanisms

○ Respiration in aquatic and terrestrial animals: Large aquatic animals have developed **gills** for respiration. Gills provide a large surface area for more efficient gas exchange, ample blood supply for gas exchange, thin membranes filaments and lamellae. In order to maximize gas exchange, bony fish use a mechanism called **countercurrent exchange** to increase the rate of diffusion throughout the gills.

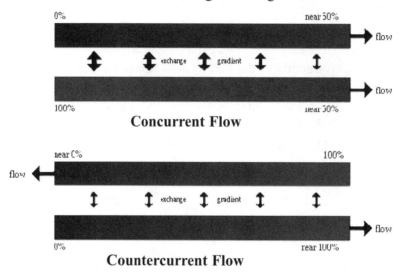

Concurrent Flow

Countercurrent Flow

○ Small, terrestrial animals may use outer surfaces as a respiratory surface. The effects of water loss dictate the development of **lungs** in larger terrestrial animals.

○ Large, terrestrial animals have developed a variety of respiratory surfaces to increase surface area for gas exchange. Lungs are present in many of these animals. Lungs are large, lobed and paired organs which are able to expand and contract through the function of the muscular **diaphragm**. The lungs lead to the **bronchi**, the **bronchioles**, and eventually to the small and numerous saclike alveoli. These surfaces are thin and moist to maximize gas exchange.

- **Excretion in aquatic and terrestrial animals**
  ○ Aquatic animals secrete ammonia directly into the environment. Ammonia is highly soluble and there is ample water for dilution of the toxic substance.
  ○ Mammals secrete urine, a solution of water and urea. Urea is produced in the liver. In the nephron, hyperosmotic urine is created which prevents dehydration and maintains blood pressure.
  ○ Birds and reptiles secrete uric acid, an energetically expensive waste product, but one that allows for more water retention.

- **The pathway and the number of chambers in the hearts of the circulatory systems in fish, amphibians and mammals vary.**
  ○ Fish have a single loop pathway of circulation and two chambers, one **atrium** and one **ventricle**.

○ Amphibians have a three chambered heart. There are two atria and one ventricle, along with a double loop circulation pathway. This allows for low pressured blood flow to the lungs and high pressured blood flow to the rest of the body.

○ In mammals, the **septum** is completely formed and there are two atria and two ventricles, as well as double loop circulation. This allows higher metabolic rates needed by endotherms.

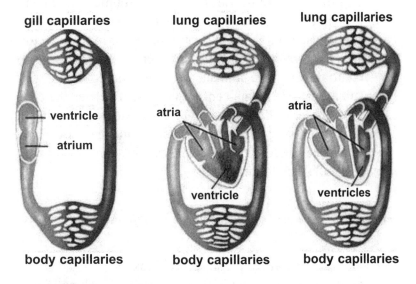

- **Thermoregulation (countercurrent exchange mechanisms) is present in aquatic and terrestrial animals.**

   ○ Countercurrent exchange mechanisms involved in temperature regulation allow animals to conserve or release heat as needed.

Homeostatic mechanisms support the theory of a common ancestor.

- Excretory systems in flatworms, earthworms, and vertebrates
   ○ Flatworms use a **nephridium** as their excretory organ. At the end of each tubule of the nephridium is a **ciliated flame cell**. Solutes are reabsorbed as fluid passes down the tubule.
   ○ The excretory system of the earthworm consists of one **nephridium** per segment. Each nephridium consists of a long tubule that begins with a ciliated opening. Fluid is carried through the opening by the beating of the **cilia** and excreted through an external pore.
   ○ All vertebrates have paired **kidneys**. The functional unit of the kidney is the nephron.
- Osmoregulation in bacteria, fish, protists and aquatic and terrestrial plants
   ○ In **halophiles** (bacteria who flourish in high salt environments), there is a constant influx of solutes into the cell through the membrane. In **non-halophiles**, growth is at its highest at low osmotic pressures.

- In freshwater fish, water diffuses into the fish because the internal environment is **hypertonic** to the surrounding water. Therefore, the fish excretes a **hypotonic** (dilute) urine to maintain body osmolarity. In marine fish, the internal environment is **hypotonic** to the environment. Therefore it tends to lose water and gain salt and actively excretes salt from the gills and excretes a small amount of hypertonic (concentrated) urine.
- In protists, **contractile vacuoles** pump excess water out of the cell. The inside of the cell is **hypertonic** to the environment, and therefore, water will flow into the cell through **osmosis**. When the vacuole is full, it pushes the water out through several pores, or may move towards the cell membrane and release fluids (or excretory wastes) through **exocytosis**.
- In terrestrial plants, the stomata are critical in regulating water loss through **transpiration**. The **large central vacuole** regulates the concentration of solutes in the cytoplasm of the cell. **Abscisic acid** regulates stomatal opening and closing to conserve water. Plants have many adaptations to conserve water including leaf modifications, sunken stomata, waxy cuticles, and stomata location.

Biological systems utilize a variety of mechanisms to adjust to disruptions to equilibrium.

- Plants and animals respond to pathogens and toxins.
  - Invertebrates use nonspecific mechanisms and lack pathogen specific defense mechanisms
  - Plants use systemic responses to pathogen defense and have a chemical response system to destroy infected cells.
  - Vertebrates use nonspecific and specific immune responses triggered by natural or synthetic invaders.
- **Dehydration** is the loss of water and salts from the body. Symptoms of dehydration include low blood pressure, decreased urine output and a fast, weak pulse.
- **Invasive species** are non-native species that disrupt ecosystems by dominating an ecosystem due to the loss of natural predators. If the invasive species outcompetes native species for resources, both those available and previously unavailable to native species.
- **Natural disasters** include earthquakes, tsunamis, floods, and hurricanes. Natural disasters are short term changes that happen to ecosystems and disrupt the natural flow of energy through the system.

The mammalian immune response contains nonspecific and specific mechanisms to maintain a dynamic homeostasis.

- The nonspecific mechanism includes physical barriers, cilia in the lungs, acidic nature of the stomach and antibacterial secretions on the skin and in tears.
- The specific mechanism includes two types of responses: **cell mediated** and **humoral**.

- **Antibodies** are produced by the body (B cells) to recognize **antigens**.
- **Antibodies** are specific to each **antigen**. Production of an antibody against antigen X will not increase the body's defense against antigen Y. However, a second exposure to antigen X will result in a more rapid and enhanced response by the humoral immune system.
- When a cell is invaded, antigens are displayed on the outside of the cell which attracts **cytotoxic T cells**.
- **B cells** produce antibodies against specific antigens.

Can you:

□ **explain** the effects of abiotic and biotic factors on community structure

□ **explain** how energy moves through trophic levels?

□ **discuss** the available energy to the producers, primary consumers, secondary consumers, and tertiary consumers?

□ **discuss** primary and secondary succession?

□ **describe** the following interspecific relationships, interspecific competition, herbivory, predation, commensalism, and mutualism?

□ **identify** specific trophic levels of a food web and integrate food chains into food webs?

□ **identify** specific examples and **discuss** how organisms exchange nutrients and wastes with their environment?

□ **discuss** how the mammalian immune system is adapted to maintain homeostasis?

2. E: Many biological processes involved in growth, reproduction and dynamic homeostasis include temporal regulation and coordination.

- Timing and coordination of specific events are necessary for the normal development of an organism, and these events are regulated by a variety of mechanisms.
- Timing and coordination of physiological events are regulated by multiple mechanisms.
- Timing and coordination of behavior are regulated by various mechanisms and are important in natural selection.

The development of an organism, and success of a population, is dependent upon the regulation, timing and coordination of several cellular events.

- **Cell differentiation** occurs during embryological development, as well as in adults during tissue repair. During cell differentiation, which is controlled by gene expression and cell signaling, a cell's size, shape, metabolic activity and responsiveness to the environment can change.
- **Transcription** in eukaryotes is primarily regulated by activators (not repressors) called **transcription factors**. These are usually proteins (or possibly RNA) that work in groups to turn genes "on" or "off". Transcription factors recognize certain nucleotide sequences before or after the gene of interest. They bind to this sequence, attract other transcription factors, and finally bind **RNA polymerase** to start transcription. Transcription factors can also amplify protein production to control gene expression.

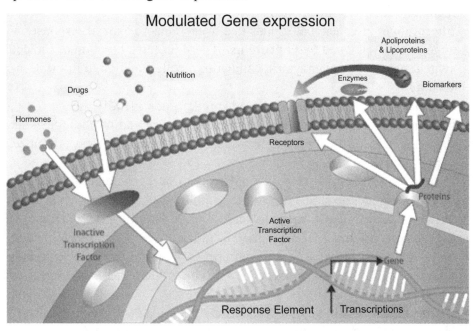

- **Homeotic genes** are any group of genes that during embryonic development control the pattern of body formation. Specific genes control their expression, usually regulated by maternal mRNA. A **transcription factor cascade** begins and differing concentrations of proteins turn on or off genes that control the pattern of body formation.

- During **embryonic induction**, one tissue affects another so that the responding tissue differentiates in a way that it normally would not. This does not require that the tissues directly touch one another, but will only occur if the responding tissue is **competent** to receive at least one chemical (probably proteins) from the inducing tissue. This is critical in neural plate, epidermal, and organ development in vertebrates.
- During seed germination, specific hormones, including **gibberillin, abscisic acid** and **ethylene** are involved in negative feedback loops. The production of these hormones is regulated by additional regulatory genes and transcription factors.
- **microRNAs** are small non-coding pieces of RNA that regulate gene expression by blocking translation or breaking down mRNAs. They are not target site specific and can regulate many different mRNAs. They are crucial in immune response, controlling the cell cycle, metabolism and cell differentiation.
- **Apoptosis**, or programmed cell death, is initiated by extracellular or intracellular signals to being a protein cascade of events that leads to the destruction of DNA in the nucleus. If apoptosis does not occur properly, cancer may result. If an abundance of apoptosis occurs, some neurological disorders may be caused. Other examples where apoptosis plays a role is in the development of fingers and toes, immune function, and in flower development, though less well understood.
- **Hibernation** and **estivation** reduce ATP turnover, change how fuel is used in the body and initiate specific changes in gene expression. **Protein synthesis** is all but stopped. However, **reversible protein** phosphorylation is a process that allows a quick return to activity when needed. Signal transduction mechanisms mediate changes in metabolism.
- **Pheromones** are chemical signals that trigger specific social responses. They appear to be regulated by **G proteins**. These proteins function as molecular switches and regulate enzymes, cellular organelle function, transcription, and secretion.
- **Visual displays** are critical in reproduction. Some identify the start of the breeding season, some provide trigger neurological and physiological changes to ready animals for the reproductive season, and some help to synchronize mating opportunities.
- In **quorum sensing**, the population density of bacteria controls gene expression. The bacteria secrete signal molecules (possibly **pheromones**). Because the bacteria can also detect these molecules, it can determine the population density based upon how much of the inducer is in the environment. When the inducer binds to the receptor it activates transcription in a **positive feedback loop**. This allows bacteria to cease production of products when there are several other bacteria in the vicinity.
- **Pollination** results in a rapid production of ethylene and petal dropping. This occurs due to the production of a specific enzyme called ACC synthase. The genes that code for this enzyme are turned on after pollination.

Can you:

- ☐ **discuss** the importance of maintaining homeostasis and how this is achieved at a molecular level?

- ☐ **explain** how regulatory mechanisms are crucial in cell differentiation?

- ☐ **describe** how homeotic genes control the pattern of body formation?

- ☐ **explain** embryonic induction?

- ☐ **discuss** how specific plant hormones affect seed germination?

- ☐ **explain** how hibernation and estivation conserve energy and **discuss** the regulatory mechanisms associated with them?

Multiple-Choice Questions

Each of the following questions is followed by four possible answers. Select the best answer for each question. The answers are given and explained in the teacher's manual that accompanies this book.

1. In the above food web, which trophic level would have the largest number of individuals?

    (A) Corn
    (B) Rabbit
    (C) Weasel
    (D) Wolf

2. In the above food web, which organism would have about 1% of the energy that was stored in the corn plants?

    (A) Decomposer
    (B) Rabbit
    (C) Weasel
    (D) Wolf

3. If a small mouse that fed solely on plants was introduced into the community with these organisms, which trophic level would be least directly impacted by the introduced species?

    (A) Corn
    (B) Rabbit
    (C) Weasel
    (D) Wolf

4. The following chart is a comparison of the metabolic response to temperature of an endotherm (15-20 lb. bird) and of an ectotherm (15-20 lb. lizard).

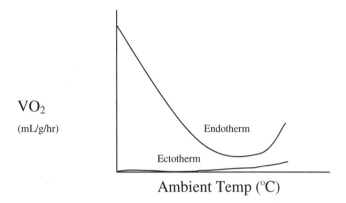

VO_2

(mL/g/hr)

Endotherm

Ectotherm

Ambient Temp (°C)

Which of the following is a plausible explanation about metabolic rate for the responses indicated on the graph?

(A) The metabolic rate of endotherms varies directly with the environment.
(B) The metabolic rate of ectotherms remains constant at all temperatures.
(C) The metabolic rate of ectotherms increases at higher temperatures.
(D) The metabolic rates of endotherms and ectotherms do not vary with temperature changes.

5. Which of the following may explain how endotherms deal with temperature changes?

(A) The energy cost of heat production is lower at lower temperatures.
(B) Active cooling mechanisms require energy and are present at high ambient temperatures.
(C) Endotherms use passive cooling mechanisms at moderate temperatures.
(D) The temperature of tissues decreases as a result of Q_{10} effects at high temperatures.

6. Interspecific relationships occur between members of differing species. Which of the following examples is not a mutualistic interspecific relationship?

(A) Clover flowers provide food for honey bees who pollinate the flowers.
(B) Small fish swim behind the sharks and eat debris that flies away from the shark's body.
(C) Sea anemone provides home for clown fish while the clown fish keeps debris away from anemone.
(D) Trychonympha in the gut of a termite is provided safety and food from termite while termite is provided with help breaking down wood by the protest.

7. Scientists working with two Paramecia species grew the two species alone in a similar culture. The results for these two alone cultures are shown in graphs 1 and 2.

Graph #1—*Paramecium caudatum* alone

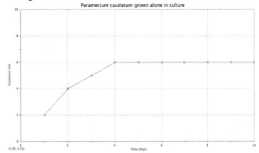

Graph #2—*Paramecium aurelia* alone

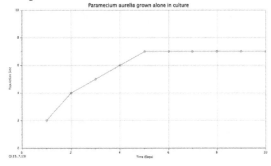

Graph #3—Two *Paramecium* species grown together

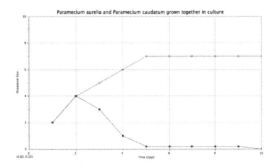

Both species of *Paramecia* were grown in the same culture and graphed the results in graph #3. What biological concept best describes the results shown in graph 3?

(A) A particular toxin increased in concentration in the environment through biological magnification that was harmful to both species of *Paramecia*.

(B) One species of *Paramecia* benefitted from the relationship and, as in commensalism, one neither was harmed nor benefitted.

(C) One *Paramecia* species, through competitive exclusion, outcompeted the other species for nutrients and flourished.

(D) The lifespan of one species of *Paramecia* is shorter than the other.

8.

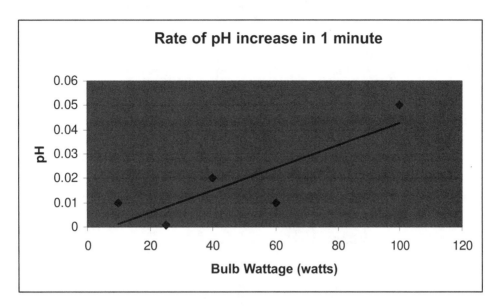

The graph shows the effect of bulb wattage on pH value in an *Elodea* plant in a sodium bicarbonate solution. Which of the following explains the change in pH of that solution?

(A) The increased temperature of the solution caused a decrease in pH and a decrease in photosynthetic rate.

(B) A bulb of approximately 25 watts will provide a neutral solution for the *Elodea* and photosynthesis will increase.

(C) As bulb wattage increases, CO_2 usage increases and the solution becomes more basic.

(D) The pH of the solution is indirectly proportional to the rate of photosynthesis in *Elodea*.

9. Photosynthesis converts CO_2 to organic compounds, as evidenced in the lab described above. Which of the following statements is true regarding photosynthesis?

(A) Carbon dioxide is fixed during the light dependent reactions of photosynthesis.

(B) The electron donor in photosynthesis is CO_2.

(C) The splitting of H_2O causes a release of H^+ ions which increases the pH of the solution during photosynthesis.

(D) The enzyme rubisco captures carbon dioxide and fixes it into energy rich molecules of glucose.

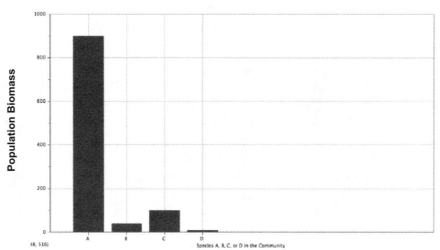

Biomass of Four Organisms in Community

10. The biomass graph shows the biomass of four different organisms in a community. In this graph, species A is most likely the

    (A)   producer
    (B)   primary consumer
    (C)   secondary consumer
    (D)   tertiary consumer

11. The biomass graph shows the biomass of four different organisms in a community. Following the information in this graph, what kind of organism is species C likely to be?

    (A)   Fern plant
    (B)   Cricket
    (C)   Robin
    (D)   Fox

12. A fire has just destroyed a pine forest ecosystem, leaving little vegetation and displacing many, if not all of the animals. What will happen in this area in the next month following the fire?

    (A)   Lichens will begin to cling to exposed rock.
    (B)   Large mammals will migrate quickly back to area to eat exposed nutrients.
    (C)   Small weedy plants and young saplings will begin to grow and take advantage of the many available nutrients.
    (D)   Deciduous trees will be established and take over the burned pine forest.

13. Plants have evolved many characteristics to avoid being consumed by herbivores. There are a variety of physical and chemical defenses present in plants. Which of the following is not a physical plant defense?

(A) Thick slippery cuticle
(B) Presence of tannin
(C) Leaf hairs
(D) Thorns on stems

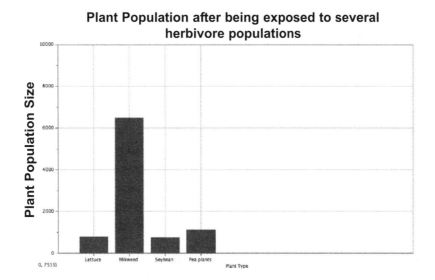

14. Several herbivore populations were allowed to feed freely on four different plant populations. After two weeks of open foraging, the plant population numbers were recorded and a graph of the data is given above. What is the most likely reason that the milkweed population is much larger than the other plants?

(A) Milkweed does not grow a sweet-tasting fruit that attracts herbivores.
(B) Milkweed plants have many sharp thorns that deter herbivorous insects.
(C) Milkweed plants release a pheromone that attracts carnivores to eat the herbivores.
(D) Milkweed produces a tannin that inhibits herbivory.

15. Some animals have evolved a defense mechanism called cryptic coloration. Examine the following example of defense characteristics. Which defense characteristic most clearly displays cryptic coloration.

(A) A poisonous coral snake has alternating black, yellow and red stripes.
(B) A moth has a gray mottled appearance that looks like tree bark.
(C) A blue jean dart frog has bright blue and red coloring patterns.
(D) A caterpillar has several sharp spines down the dorsal side.

16. Some animals have evolved a defense mechanism called aposomatic coloration. Examine the following example of defense characteristics. Which defense characteristic most clearly displays aposomatic coloration?

(A) A bullfrog has a dark green color that looks like plants leaves.
(B) A skunk has bold black and white markings that are very distinct.
(C) A rattlesnake has a dark brown color that looks like rock.
(D) A king cobra has broadened neck for increased mouth expansion.

17. Which of the following cells will be able to eliminate wastes and obtain nutrients more efficiently and why?

	Surface Area (cm$_2$)	Volume (mL)
A	150	125
B	100	50
C	6	1
D	200	200

(A) Cell A is most efficient due to its high surface area.
(B) Cell B is most efficient due to its moderate surface are and volume.
(C) Cell C is most efficient due to its high surface area to volume ratio.
(D) Cell D is most efficient due to its identical surface area and volume.

18. Which of the following properties of water is most responsible for the fact that oceans tend to moderate temperatures along coastlines?

(A) Cohesion
(B) Adhesion
(C) Surface tension
(D) Hydrogen bonding

19. Which of the following waste products is most appropriate for reptiles dwelling in dry, arid conditions?

(A) Urea
(B) Ammonia
(C) Uric acid
(D) Creatinine

20. The following graph shows the effects of sugar concentration on potato cell mass.

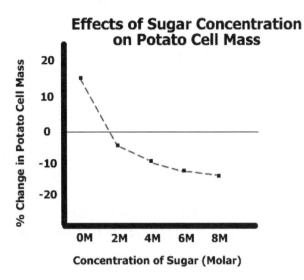

Which of the following is true about the graph?

(A)   The 0 M solution was hypertonic to the potato cells due to the increased percentage.

(B)   The 0.2 M solution was isotonic to the potato cells as it has the smallest percent change in mass.

(C)   The 0.8 M concentration is hypotonic to the potato cells as it has the greatest decrease in mass.

(D)   The potato cells are hypotonic to the 0.4 M and 0.6 M solutions due to the fact that there was a decreased percentage change in mass.

21. Which of the following cell organelle structures is correctly matched to its function?

(A)   The folds in the mitochondria contain a folded inner membrane for increased ATP production.

(B)   The transport proteins on the outside of the cell membrane are shaped specifically to assist in cell to cell recognition processes.

(C)   The lysosome is not membrane bound so that the enzymes it holds may be easily released during phagocytosis.

(D)   The nuclear membrane is solid to prevent pathogens from entering the nucleus and harming the nuclear DNA.

22. Shortly after microscopically observing the open stomata of a Jade plant, the stomata became closed. Which of the following environmental factors could have caused this physiological change?

(A) There was a decreased level of CO_2 inside the leaf.
(B) The light intensity of the environment increased.
(C) The humidity level of the surrounding environment increased.
(D) Abscisic acid was produced inside the plant.

23. Which of the following physiological responses will occur immediately after your afternoon meal of chicken nuggets, French fries, and a milk shake at McDonalds?

(A) Your body will secrete glucagon to convert glycogen into glucose.
(B) You will metabolize the fat from the French fries immediately.
(C) Your body will secrete insulin in response to the high carbohydrate meal.
(D) Your blood glucose levels will decrease due to the protein content of the chicken.

24. Plants often exhibit responses to photoperiodism, or changes in light and dark in a 24 hour period. Based on the data table, which of the following plants is most likely a plant that will flower when a critical night length is reached or if it is interrupted it is by a far red flash of light?

Plant species	Flowering Season in middle latitudes
Chrysanthemums	Late Summer
Goldenrods	Autumn
Irises	Spring
Hollyhocks	Early Summer
Poinsettias	Late Summer
Ragweed	Autumn
Clover	Spring

(A) Irises
(B) Hollyhocks
(C) Chrysanthemums
(D) Clover

25. Which of the following is an adaptation of an organism in an arid, dry environment?

(A) Stomata located on the tops of leaves
(B) Excretion of ammonia as a nitrogenous waste
(C) Thin non-waxy cuticles
(D) Lack of sweat glands

26. Which of the following behaviors is an example of kinesis?

   (A)   Sowbugs scurry when a rock is picked up
   (B)   Moths move towards an outdoor light at night
   (C)   Female mosquitoes find mammals by moving towards heat
   (D)   Sharks move toward food when the current brings odors to them

27. Which of the following regulatory mechanisms is correctly matched to the environment?

   (A)   Freshwater fish excrete hypertonic urine in large volumes to maintain body osmolarity.
   (B)   Halophiles maintain a constant influx of solutes through their cell membranes to maintain osmolarity.
   (C)   Protists use contractile vacuoles to pump water into the cell to maintain osmolarity.
   (D)   Stomata are located on the top of the leaf on raised dimples on the leaf to limit evapotranspiration.

28. Which of the following types of cells is most crucial in maintaining the response depicted below?

   (A)   Cytotoxic T cells
   (B)   B cells
   (C)   Macrophages
   (D)   Antigens

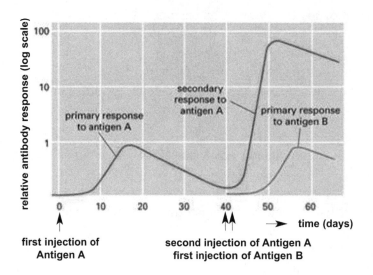

29. Which of the following offers the best explanation for the graph above?

   (A)   The secondary response the antigen A takes longer than the primary response to antigen B.
   (B)   The primary response to antigen A takes longer than the secondary response to antigen A.
   (C)   The primary response the antigen B is faster due to the fact that antigen A was already recognized by the body.
   (D)   The concentration of antibodies specific to antigen B is the most plentiful.

30.

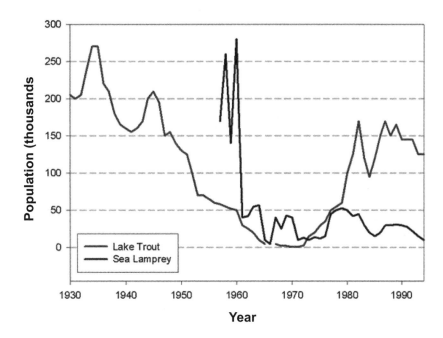

Lake trout and sea lamprey populations are both present in Lake Superior. Which of the following is true about the ecosystem dynamics between 1930 and 1990?

(A) A healthy lake trout population was affected slightly by competition from the sea lamprey around 1960.

(B) An increase in the lake trout population initiated a decrease in the sea lamprey population in 1960.

(C) The quick decline of the sea lamprey was most likely due to an outside influence other than competition from the lake trout.

(D) The lake trout and sea lamprey are living in equilibrium around 1970.

Free-Response Questions for Big Idea #2

Directions: On the AP biology exam, there will be 8 free-response questions. These questions address a varying number of questions, and will therefore be worth a variety of points. Free response questions may be worth between 2 - 10 points. For these questions, follow the given instructions and note the boldfaced words. Take a few minutes to brainstorm your response to the more in depth questions to organize your thoughts. Write clear complete responses in complete sentences for each question. Grading rubrics for these practice free-response questions are provided in the teacher's manual that accompanies this review book.

1.   **10 points are possible on this question.**

Thompson Forest is a North American temperate deciduous forest. In the fall of 1970, acres of this forest were clear cut. Consequently, the ecosystem changed over the next forty years.

(a)   **Identify** and **define** the type of succession that would occur after the fire.
(b)   **Describe** what the community structure might look like one year after the clear cutting and in the present time.
(c)   **Identify** and **discuss** THREE factors that could affect how ecological succession occurred in the later years following the clear cutting.

2.   **10 points are possible on this question.**

Both food webs and food chains show representations of how energy moves through an ecosystem.

(a)   **Draw** a diagram of a four-member, terrestrial food chain and **describe** the trophic levels of each member of that food chain.
(b)   **Explain** mathematically how the energy of one trophic level moves and changes between the lowest level of the food chain and the top level of the food chain.
(c)   **Discuss** TWO possible effects on the food chain if an invasive species was introduced into the ecosystem.

3.   **4 points are possible on this question.**

Identify the difference between an antigen and an antibody and **discuss** how the body's response to an antigen the second time is different than it was during the first exposure.

4.   **2 points are possible on this question.**

Organisms obtain nutrients and eliminate waste products efficiently by maintaining high surface area to volume ratios at the cellular level. **Explain** this statement using mathematical evidence and **describe** ONE specific example in a plant OR animal of a structure that increase the surface area of a cell.

5.   **3 points are possible on this question.**

Using a specific organelle as an example, describe two advantages of compartmentalization in the eukaryotic cell

NO TESTING MATERIAL PRINTED ON THIS PAGE

GO ON TO THE NEXT PAGE

BIG IDEA!

Big Idea #3: Living systems store, retrieve, transmit, and respond to information essential to life processes

Key Terms for this section:

- Allele
- Alternative splicing
- Aneuploidy
- Cell plate
- Centromere
- Cleavage furrow
- Codominance
- Conjugation
- Crossing over
- Cytokinesis
- DNA
- DNA ligase
- DNA methylation
- DNA polymerase
- DNA replication
- Epistasis
- Euchromatin
- Genotype
- Helicase
- Hemizygous
- Heterochromatin
- Heterozygous
- Homologous chromosomes
- Homozygous
- Incomplete dominance
- Independent assortment

- Inducible operon
- Kinetochore
- Lagging strand
- Leading strand
- Linked traits
- Lysogenic cycle
- Lytic cycle
- Meiosis
- Mendelian genetics
- Mitosis
- Nondisjunction
- Nucleotide
- Operons
- Phenotype
- Pilus
- Polygenic inheritance
- Polyploidy
- Purine
- Pyrimidine
- Repressible operon
- RNA
- Sex-linked traits
- Splicing
- Synapsis
- Telomere
- Transduction
- Transformation

3A: Heritable information provides for continuity of life.

- **DNA, and in some cases RNA, is the primary source of heritable information.**
- **In eukaryotes, heritable information is passed to the next generation via processes that include the cell cycle and mitosis or meiosis plus fertilization.**
- **The chromosomal basis of inheritance provides an understanding of the pattern of passage of genes from parents to offspring.**
- **The inheritance pattern of many traits cannot be explained by simple Mendelian genetics.**

The structure of DNA makes it a desirable molecule as the source of genetic information.

- The work of many scientists led to great discoveries in the area of understanding DNA to be the genetic material and isolating the structure and role of DNA in cells.

Scientist	Contribution to Understanding the Function and Structure of DNA
Frederick Griffith	• Transformation of genetic material is possible through use of two pneumonia strains
Oswald Avery, Maclyn McCarty, Colin MacLeod	• Repeated Griffith's experiments to find that the transforming agent was DNA
Alfred Hershey and Martha Chase	• Used bacteriophages to isolate that the DNA from the phage transforms the bacterial host
Erwin Chargaff	• The percentage of the four types of nucleotides is different in different organisms • Percent of adenine nucleotides is the same as the percent of thymine nucleotides • Percent of cytosine nucleotides is the same as percent of guanine nucleotides
Maurice Wilkins	• Operated a lab where X-ray crystallography was conducted to analyze molecules
Rosalind Franklin	• Took the first X-ray picture of DNA
James Watson and Francis Crick	• Proposed the double-helix model of DNA based upon contributions of earlier scientists • Proposed semi-conservative model of replication, but lacked supporting evidence
Matthew Meselson and Franklin Stahl	• Used isotopes of nitrogen to demonstrate that DNA replication could not be conservative or dispersive • Evidence that DNA replication is semi-conservative
George Beadle and Edward Tatum	Using bread mold were able to discern that each gene appears to be responsible for making one enzyme that is needed for a biological process

- DNA and RNA are **nucleic acid** molecules. They are constructed from nucleotides.
- A **nucleotide** has a phosphate group, a five carbon sugar, and a nitrogenous base.
- The five carbon sugar in DNA is **deoxyribose** and the five carbon sugar in RNA is **ribose**.
- The nitrogenous bases in DNA are **adenine, thymine, cytosine** and **guanine**.
- The nitrogenous bases in RNA are **adenine, uracil, cytosine,** and **guanine**.
- Adenine and guanine have two fused carbon and nitrogen rings and are **purines**. The purines are larger than the **pyrimidines**.
- Cytosine, thymine, and uracil are pyrimidines. They have single carbon and nitrogen ring structure.
- RNA is generally a single strand of nucleotides.
- DNA is a double strand of nucleotides.
- In the two **complementary** strands of DNA, a purine of one strand must bond with a pyrimidine of the other strand. Adenine pairs with thymine. Cytosine pairs with guanine.
- The two strands of the DNA double strand are **antiparallel**. One strand runs from its 3' to 5' end and the other goes from 5' to 3'.
- The shape of the double DNA strand is a **double helix**. **Hydrogen bonds** between bases in the opposing strands reinforce the helical structure.

All present and past living organisms have RNA or DNA as the genetic material.

- The first living organisms had RNA as the genetic material. The complex structure of DNA would have made it improbable in the early earth.
- Over time the RNA genomes were not favored by natural selection and a DNA genome became prevalent.
- All extant organisms (prokaryote and eukaryote) have a DNA genome.
- While not considered living organisms, viruses can have DNA or RNA genomes.

DNA can serve as the genetic material because it can be copied by DNA replication preceding cell division.

- The genome of an organism is copied entirely during **DNA replication**.
- DNA replication happens in the nucleus in a eukaryote and in the cytosol in a prokaryote.
- DNA replication is **semiconservative**. The two parental DNA strands separate and each one is copied to make a new strand. The two DNA double helices that form at the end of the process each have one parental strand of DNA and one new strand of DNA.
- DNA replication begins at a **replication fork**. In the fork, a bubble forms as the two DNA strands are separated.
- **Helicase** is an enzyme that separates the two parental DNA strands so that each one can be copied.

- Once the two parental DNA strands are separated. **Single strand binding proteins** adhere to each parental DNA strand so that the complementary bases on the opposing strands do not come to back together and prevent the replication process.
- **DNA polymerase** is an enzyme that adds free DNA nucleotides to free 3' end of a growing DNA strand. The DNA polymerase builds both of the new DNA strands. One of the new strands of DNA is called the **leading strand** and one of the new strands is called the **lagging strand**.
- The leading strand of DNA is growing toward its 3' end. So, the DNA polymerase can easily move down the template strand and build the new strand by simply adding one nucleotide at a time to the 3' side. It continues elongating the leading strand until the entire genome is copied.
- The lagging strand of DNA is growing along a template that runs from 5' to 3'. So, the antiparallel nature of DNA only allows the lagging strand to grow from its 3' to 5' end. DNA polymerase cannot add nucleotides individually on the 5' end. Small fragments called **Okazaki fragments** grow in the formation of the lagging strand of DNA. These fragments allow the DNA polymerase to move against the direction of the growing DNA strand and add nucleotides to the 3' end of the fragments. Then, **DNA ligase** builds covalent bonds between the adjacent Okazaki fragments to seal the breaks in the lagging strand.
- The final products of DNA replication are two identical DNA strands. This process allows the cell to have two complete copies of its genome before beginning a cell division process.

Organisms are able to use cellular division processes to increase cell number and for reproduction.

- Prokaryote organisms are unicellular. Cellular division is only used for reproduction. The process that prokaryotes use for reproduction is called **binary fission**. In this process, after the two DNA strands are formed from replication, there is a random division of the remainder of the cell. Each new cell gets a random subset of the organelles and cytosol and one complete copy of the genome.
- Eukaryotes use **mitosis** to increase cell number in multicellular organisms and for reproduction in unicellular organisms. Mitosis produces two daughter cells that are genetically identical to the parent cell.
- Eukaryotes use **meiosis** for sexual reproduction to make daughter cells that are half the chromosome number of the parent cell and are genetically unique.
- The **cell cycle** describes the basic life of a cell. It begins when a cell forms from a division process until the cell divides. It includes two stages: the mitotic stage where cell division occurs and interphase where the cell does basic cell activities.

- **Interphase** is much longer than the division stage of the cell cycle. There are three stages of interphase: G1, S, and G2. During G1, the cell does its basic metabolism and normal cellular activity. During the S phase, DNA replication occurs so that the cell has two complete copies of the genome prior to division. During G2, the organelles are copied so that there are a large enough number of organelles if the cells randomly divided.
- During division, there is both nuclear division and cellular division. The nuclear division is the separation of the chromosomes during mitosis or meiosis. The cellular division is called **cytokinesis**. Cytokinesis is the division of the cytosol, organelles, and plasma membrane of the two daughter cells.
- In animal cells, a **cleavage furrow** forms as microfilaments of the cytoskeleton wrap around the boundary of the two daughter cells. The microfilaments pinch inward until the two cells pinch apart. The cytosol and organelles randomly divide in this pinching process.
- In plant cells, a **cell plate** forms at the boundary between the two daughter cells. The cell plate forms as vesicles filled with cellulose align along the boundary. These vesicles fuse together making a small cellulose island at the cellular boundary. This cell plate continues to elongate until it becomes continuous with the cell wall of the plant cells. The cytosol and organelles divide randomly in this division process.

Organisms are able to use mitosis for asexual reproduction or to increase cell number.

- The process of mitosis describes how the chromosomes containing the copied DNA are divided into the two daughter cells. The five stages of mitosis are prophase, prometaphase, metaphase, anaphase, and telophase.
- During prophase, the chromosomes condense and become visible under the light microscope. In animal cells, the centrioles begin to move apart. The mitotic spindle forms. Spindle fibers extend from the centrioles. The nucleolus is no longer visible.
- During prometaphase, the nuclear envelope fragments and the chromosomes attach to the spindle fibers at the **kinetochores**. The centrioles continue to move apart until they are positioned at opposite ends of the cell.
- During metaphase, the spindle fibers push the chromosomes to the center of the cell. The chromosomes align along an invisible line called the metaphase plate.
- During anaphase, the spindle fibers shorten. As these fibers shorten, they pull the chromosomes apart at their centromeres. The two sister chromatids are separated, one chromatid moves to each pole.
- During telophase, the chromosomes uncoil and are no longer visible. Cytokinesis begins during this stage of nuclear division. The nuclear envelope and nucleolus both reappear.
- The final products of mitosis are two genetically identical cells that are exact genetic replicas of the parent cell. Mitosis can be used as a mechanism of asexual reproduction.

Organisms are able to use meiosis to make haploid genetically unique daughter cells for sexual reproduction.

- Meiosis accompanies sexual reproduction in organisms. It allows for genetic variability and a decrease in chromosome number.
- The products of meiosis are haploid (half the chromosome number of the parent cell) and genetically unique.
- Before meiosis, the DNA is copied in the S phase of interphase. There are two divisions in meiosis with only one interphase and DNA replication. Without an interkinesis, the chromosome number is halved by the two division processes.
- There are eight stages of meiosis: prophase I, metaphase I, anaphase I, and telophase I, prophase II, metaphase II, anaphase II, and telophase II.
- During prophase I, the chromosomes condense and become visible under the light microscope. The nuclear envelope breaks down. The nucleolus disappears. The centrioles begin to move apart and the mitotic spindle forms. The two homologous chromosomes pair up in the process in the **synapsis**. While paired, a piece of one homologous chromosome exchanges fragments with the other homolog in the process of **crossing-over**.
- Crossing-over is the most important process to ensure that there is genetic diversity at the end of meiosis. **Chiasmata** can occur randomly along the two homologous chromosomes. Chiasmata are places where the two homologs cross over one another. It can happen at any location and at any number of locations along the two homologs. During this cross-over process, genetic information is exchanged between the two homologs. It ensures that each sister chromatid in the tetrad is genetically unique.
- During metaphase I, the chromosome pairs attach to the spindle fibers at the kinetochores. The spindle fibers push the chromosomes to the cell's equator. The chromosome pairs align along the equator. These chromosomes line up randomly.
- During anaphase I, the spindle fibers shorten. As the spindle fibers shorten, the homologous chromosomes are separated. The random separation of chromosomes helps to give more diversity. It is unlikely that only paternal or maternal chromosomes will end up in each daughter nucleus. This random separation of the maternal and paternal chromosomes is independent assortment.
- During telophase I, cytokinesis begins. The chromosomes uncoil and are no longer visible. The nucleolus reappears. The nuclear envelope reforms. The two nuclei still have replicated chromosomes. However, they only have one copy of each homologous pair. So, these nuclei are haploid.
- Without an interkinesis, the two cells both undergo meiosis II.
- During prophase II, the chromosomes condense and become visible under the light microscope. The nucleolus disappears and the nuclear envelope fragments. The mitotic spindle forms as the two centrioles move apart.
- During metaphase II, the individual chromosomes attach to the spindle fibers at the kinetochores. The spindle fibers push the chromosomes to the equator. The chromosomes line up randomly and individually along the cell's equator.

- During anaphase II, the spindle fibers shorten pulling the sister chromatids apart.
- During telophase II, the chromosomes uncoil and are no longer visible. The nuclear envelopes reform in the daughter cells. Cytokinesis begins.
- At the conclusion of meiosis, there are four haploid daughter cells that are genetically unique.

The chromosome theory of heredity and fundamentals of genetics describes how genetic information is passed via chromosomes.

- **Walter Sutton** described the chromosome theory of heredity. It states that the genetic material is located on the chromosomes.
- **Gregor Mendel** is the father of genetics. He worked with pea plants and determined that individuals have two copies of genes that are randomly segregated during gamete formation. He also said that when an individual has two different forms of a gene, one will be dominant and one will be recessive.
- Dominant alleles are always expressed and recessive alleles are expressed only when not present with a dominant form.
- The different forms of a gene that are possible are called **alleles.**
- In most genetic cases, every individual has two alleles for a given trait. These two alleles are the genotype of that individual. When an individual has two of the same alleles, it is **homozygous** and when an individual has two different alleles, it is **heterozygous**.
- The physical expression of these alleles is called the **phenotype**.
- Mendelian traits have one dominant allele and one recessive allele.
- Many traits are not inherited in a strictly Mendelian pattern.
  - When there are more than two possible alleles, it is called **multiple alleles**. Each individual still has two alleles of the possible ones.
  - During **incomplete dominance**, neither of the two alleles is dominant. So, neither allele is strictly expressed in the heterozygotes. The heterozygous individuals have a phenotype that is a blend of the two homozygous phenotypes.
  - During **codominance**, both alleles are dominant and must be expressed in the heterozygous individuals. The heterozygotes have some a spotty appearance from the presence of both homozygous phenotypes occurring simultaneously.
  - **Polygenic traits** are due to the interactions of several genes. The traits show a wide range of phenotypes.
  - **Epistasis** occurs when the alleles at a second locus affect the appearance of the trait at a first locus.
  - **Sex-linked traits** are located on the sex chromosomes. Most sex-linked traits occur on the X chromosome. So, males only have one copy of these X-linked traits and are hemizygous. Recessive sex-linked traits occur more frequently in males since they only need one copy to show the recessive trait.
  - **Linked genes** are located on the same chromosome and are inherited together.

Can you:

□ **describe** the experiments that help to uncover the structure of DNA?

□ **explain** the structure of DNA?

□ **explain** the process of DNA replication?

□ **explain** the roles of helicase, DNA polymerase, and DNA ligase?

□ **identify** the electron acceptors in the different energy capturing processes?

□ **compare** and **contrast** the formation of the leading strand and the lagging strand during DNA replication?

□ **explain** the cell cycle?

□ **explain** cytokinesis?

□ **compare and contrast** the process of cytokinesis in animal cell and in a plant cell\

□ **describe** the daughter cells of mitosis?

□ **describe** the cellular actions in the various stages of mitosis?

□ **compare and contrast** mitosis and meiosis?

□ **explain** the cellular events during each stage of meiosis?

□ **explain** how synapsis and crossing over occur in meiosis?

□ **explain** crossing over and independent assortment contribute to the variation?

□ **explain** how the reduction in chromosome number happens in meiosis?

□ **explain** how traits are inherited?

□ **compare and contrast** Mendelian genetics, incomplete dominance, codominance, multiple alleles, polygenic inheritance, epistasis, sex-linked traits, linked traits?

3.B: Expression of genetic information involves cellular and molecular mechanisms.

- Gene regulation results in differential gene expression, leading to cell specialization.
- A variety of intercellular and intracellular signal transmissions mediate gene expression.

Gene regulation allows for differential gene expression and cell specialization.

- Prokaryotes have limited mechanisms for gene control. Prokaryotes have single circular chromosomes which limits the degree of regulation.
- Eukaryotes have many mechanisms for gene regulation. There are many specialized cells present in multicellular eukaryotes.

Prokaryotes use operons for gene regulation.

- **Jacob and Manod** were the first researchers to uncover an operon system when they discovered the lactose operon.
- **Operons** use a binding site on the DNA next to the **promoter** for transcription. This site is called the **operator**. Proteins called **repressors** are able to bind to the operator. When a repressor is attached to the operator, the gene or gene system is inactive. When a repressor is absent at the operator, the gene or gene system is active and being transcribed.
- Operons can be inducible or repressible. **Inducible operons** are generally turned off and only become active when the repressor is lifted. The repressor is lifted when an inducer binds to the repressor causing a conformational change in the repressor. This conformational change will prevent the repressor from being attached to the operator.
- **Repressible operons** are generally turned on and only inactivated when the repressor binds. A corepressor binds to the repressor causing a conformational change of the repressor. The new shape of the repressor makes it attach to the operator and block transcription making the gene inactive.

Eukaryotes have more complicated genomes which allow for many mechanisms for gene regulation.

- Eukaryotes have many chromosomes. Many eukaryotes have diploid cells with two sets of chromosomes. Eukaryotic chromosomes have repetitive ends called **telomeres** and a central area called a **centromere**. Eukaryotes have **histone** proteins in the chromosomes that help with the compaction of the DNA.
- In eukaryotes, the condensed chromatin like during mitosis is called **heterochromatin**. **Euchromatin** is the uncoiled genome regions.
- Some DNA stays condensed in the heterochromatin form and it prevents the DNA in that region from being transcribed. The RNA polymerase cannot fit into the coiled up DNA to copy it into RNA.

- In **DNA methylation**, methyl groups are added to the nucleotides which block the RNA polymerase and makes genes inactive. This regulation method can be used for long-term gene inactivation. This long-term gene inactivation can be passed to offspring and is responsible for genomic imprinting.
- With **histone acetylation**, acetyl groups are added to the histones in the chromosomes. The histones loosen the grip on the DNA making it uncoil even farther and increase the rate of the gene activity.
- **Control elements** like the TATA box and the CAAT box are regions of DNA near the promoter. Transcription factors and other proteins bind to these regions. When these proteins bind to the control elements, they increase the binding rate of the RNA polymerase to the promoter and increase the gene activity. Proteins can also bind to these regions that block binding of the RNA polymerase and make the gene inactive.
- When the DNA is transcribed into RNA in eukaryotes, the RNA transcript must be altered to move into the cytosol for translation. A **modified guanine** is added to the 5' end of the RNA transcript. A **poly A tail** is added to the 3' end of the RNA transcript. These protective end caps can be removed to reduce the gene activity.
- Also, during the alterations to the RNA transcript, noncoding regions of the RNA called **introns** must be removed by a protein and RNA complex called a spliceosome. During **alternative splicing**, different regions of the RNA transcript are cleaved as introns.
- After translation, chaperone proteins can be blocked to prevent protein folding.
- Excess polypeptides can be tagged with **ubiquitin** so that a **proteasome** will break them up and reduce gene activity.

Many chemical regulators affect gene expression.

- There are local and long distance chemical regulators. Local regulators are secreted from a cell and affect a target cell in close proximity. Long distance regulators travel via the bloodstream to affect target cells that can be far away from the secretory cells.
- There are many local types of local regulators.
  - In **synaptic signaling**, neurotransmitters travel from the axon terminal of a neuron to the target cell. These signals cross the synaptic cleft and bind to proteins on the surface of the target cell.
  - In **paracrine signaling**, one cell secretes a chemical that travels to an adjacent cell as the target cell.
  - In **autocrine signaling**, the cell that secretes the chemical is also the target of that chemical.
- The primary type of long distance regulator is a hormone. In plants, hormones can travel across cells, through the cell wall area, or through the air to reach the target cells. In animals, the hormones travel via the bloodstream to reach the target cell
- The two primary classes of hormones are **amino acid derivative or protein hormones and steroid hormones**.

- Amino acid derivatives are either altered amino acids like T_3 or norepinephrine or proteins like insulin. These protein hormones have large, complicated shapes. There are often polar regions in these proteins. The size and polarity prevents these protein hormones from being able to cross the lipid bilayer of the plasma membrane. These proteins bind to surface proteins on the target cell. They are fast acting, and the responses are often dramatic and brief.
- Steroid hormones are lipids that are nonpolar and fairly small for an organic molecule. These nonpolar steroids can cross the lipid bilayer of the membrane and cross into the interior of the target cell. These lipids bind to a binding site on the inside of the cell. These hormones are slower, but the response often has a longer duration.

Can you:

☐ **describe** the structure of the operon system?

☐ **explain** the difference between an inducible and a repressible operon?

☐ **explain** how chromatin compaction affects gene activity in eukaryotes?

☐ **describe** how DNA methylation and histone acetylation affect gene activity in eukaryotes?

☐ **explain** how the RNA transcript is altered to the mRNA in eukaryotes?

☐ **explain** how alternative splicing occurs in eukaryotes?

☐ **discuss** how alternative splicing and end cap removal can be used to regulate gene activity in eukaryotes?

☐ **describe** how transcription factors and control regions can affect gene activity in eukaryotes?

☐ **compare and contrast** local and long distance regulatory mechanisms?

☐ **compare and contrast** autocrine, paracrine and synaptic signaling?

☐ **compare and contrast** protein hormones and steroid hormones?

3. C: The processing of genetic information is imperfect and is a source of genetic variation.

- **Changes in genotypes can result in changes in phenotypes.**
- **Biological systems have multiple processes that increase genetic variation.**
- **Viral replication results in genetic variation, and viral infection can introduce genetic variation into hosts.**

Errors occur during replication that affect characteristics.

- There are errors in the DNA replication process. These errors are called **mutations**. If these errors affect a single gene or protein, they are **point mutations** or **gene mutations**.
    - Sometimes a single base or a few bases are replaced with an incorrect base. These errors are called **substitutions**. If the substitution is in the third slot of a codon, often it doesn't affect the protein. If it is placed where it does code for a different amino acid, it can greatly affect the protein like is the case with sickle cell anemia.
    - **Insertions** occur when one or a few bases are added to the DNA. If the added base number is not a multiple of three, a frameshift can happen which alters each amino acid in the protein.
    - **Deletions** occur when one or few bases are removed from the DNA. If the deleted base number is not a multiple of three, a frameshift can happen which alters each amino acid in the protein.
- Errors can occur in meiosis that affect a large portion of a chromosome or an entire chromosome. These errors are called **chromosomal mutations**.
    - A cell can end meiosis with an extra chromosome, one less chromosome, or a complete set of extra chromosomes (in plants only). These chromosome number errors are called **nondisjunctions**.
    - Nondisjunction occurs when chromosomes fail to separate properly during meiosis I or meiosis II.
    - **Aneuploidy** occurs when there is one extra or one two few chromosomes.
    - **Polyploidy** occurs when there is one or more extra sets of chromosomes.
    - **Deletions** occur when a large section of chromosome is broken off and the genes from that area are lost.
    - **Inversions** occur when the sequence of genes on the chromosome are shuffled.
    - **Translocations** occur when a piece of one chromosome breaks off and is attached to another chromosome.

Biological organisms have many mechanisms for genetic diversity.

- **Mutations** introduce genetic diversity by altering the genetic material. The DNA polymerase works to correct errors during replication. However, some of the errors are not caught in the proof-reading process and persist and become mutations. Mutations can be harmless. However, mutations can disrupt phenotypes and introduce new alleles and phenotypes.
- **Meiosis** and sexual reproduction introduce genetic diversity. Crossing-over is where a piece of one homologous chromosome is exchanged with a piece of the other homolog. There is a random exchange of genetic material at a region on the chromosomes called the chiasmata. Independent assortment occurs where the chromosome pairs align randomly in metaphase I and separate randomly in anaphase II. It ensures that there is juggling of the maternal and paternal chromosomes in each daughter cell.
- **Random fertilization** occurs in many animals where there is some randomness to the binding of the sperm the egg. Which sperm and egg are involved is not directed. There is some randomness to both the egg and sperm selection in the zygote.
- There are mechanisms that affect genetic variation in prokaryotes only.
  - During **transformation**, foreign DNA is absorbed by the cell and can exist in a plasmid or become part of the genome.
  - During **conjugation**, a cytoplasmic bridge called a **pilus** forms that connects to prokaryotic cells. One bacterium that has a plasmid replicates the plasmid and then it passes through the pilus to the second cell. This way each cell has a copy of the plasmid and the genes on that plasmid.
  - During **transduction**, viruses pass some foreign bacterial DNA to their host. The virus brings a piece of bacterial DNA from a previous host that becomes part of the genome as the virus enters its lysogenic cycle.

Viruses can affect genetic information.

- Viruses are nonliving cell-like bodies with simple structures. They have a protein coat and genetic material on the interior. The genetic material can be double-stranded DNA, single-stranded DNA, double-stranded RNA, or single-stranded RNA
- Viruses infect hosts and utilize hosts for reproduction of the viral genome. Viruses are incapable of reproducing without a host cell. The host cell is transformed into producing the viral genetic material and proteins and assembling the new viruses.
- During the **lytic cycle**, the virus lands on the surface of the host cell. The genetic material is inserted into the host cell. The viral genetic material transforms the host cell. The host cell then makes viral genetic material and proteins.
- During the **lysogenic cycle**, viral DNA becomes part of the host cell genome and is copied with every host cell reproduction.

Can you:

☐ **describe** how mutations occur?

☐ **explain** the difference between point mutations and chromosomal mutations ?

☐ **identify and discuss** the following point mutations: substitutions, insertions, and deletions?

☐ **explain** how nondisjunctions occur?

☐ **compare and contrast** aneuploidy and polyploidy

☐ **identify and discuss** the following chromosomal mutations: deletions, inversions, and translocations?

☐ **explain** how meiosis provides genetic variation?

☐ **explain** how mutations provide genetic variation?

☐ **explain** how random fertilization provides genetic variation?

☐ **explain** how transformation provides genetic variation?

☐ **explain** how conjugation provides genetic variation?

☐ **explain** how transduction provides genetic variation?

☐ **discuss** the viral genome and viral reproduction?

☐ **compare and contrast** the lytic cycle and the lysogenic cycle of virus?

3. D: Cells communicate by generating, transmitting and receiving chemical signals.

- **Cell communication processes share common features that reflect a shared evolutionary history.**
- **Cells communicate with each other through direct contact with other cells or from a distance via chemical signaling.**
- **Signal transduction pathways link signal reception with cellular response.**
- **Changes in signal transduction pathways can alter cellular response.**

Cell to cell communication can occur by cell to cell contact, as well as at the local or long distance level at the cellular, organismal or ecosystem level.

- Cells must communicate to coordinate their activities
- Cells communicate by direct contact through cellular junctions or by the signal molecule dissolving in the cytoplasm.
- Cells communicate through **messenger molecules** that are released in the local vicinity of the **regulatory cells** and the **target cells**.
- Interleukins, a type of cytokine molecule, are released by white blood cells (and other cells) to act on white blood cells (and other cells). A few specific examples of interleukins are listed below:

Source	Target Cell	Function
Macrophages	Macrophages	Inflammation/Fever
Macrophages	T cells	Inflammation
T cells/B cells	B cells	Increased production of B cells
Phagocytes	T cells/B cells	Production of natural killer cells

- **Plasmodesmata** are specialized cellular structures for communication in plants. **Phloem loading** may occur via plasmodesmata.
  - ○ Transport of proteins and mRNA between cells
  - ○ **Chaperonins** may partially unfold proteins to allow them to be transported
- Short distance communication is evidenced by neurotransmitters, plant immune response, quorum sensing in bacteria and morphogens
  - ○ Neurons release neurotransmitters to a **target cell** across a **synapse**.

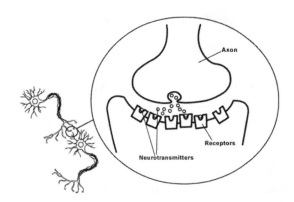

- Plants use cell communication to respond to pathogens and insects.
  - Plants do not produce antibodies or T-cell responses
  - Plants secrete chemical compounds to make them less attractive
  - Some plant parts are disposable so this is an option for plant immune system response
  - Receptors on plant cells identify pathogens and trigger elicitors which trigger **apoptosis** in some plant cells.
- Long distance communication is evidenced by the endocrine system, including insulin, human growth hormone, thyroid secretions, testosterone and estrogen

Unicellular and multicellular organisms work in similar, yet unique, ways.

- Bacteria use chemical messengers to communicate with nearby cells to regulate population density.
- Pheromones in unicellular organisms trigger reproduction and other developmental pathways.
  - **Pheromones** are chemical signals that elicit a social response.
- Bacteria respond to stimuli and move via external signals.
- Temperature helps to determine the sex of offspring in some vertebrate organisms.
- DNA repair mechanisms are controlled by external signals.
- Epinephrine signals glycogen breakdown in mammals.

Signals must be created and received in order for a response to occur.

- Chemical messengers include **peptides** or **proteins**. They are any compound that serves to transmit messages between secretory cells and target cells.
- **Receptor proteins** are located in cell membranes, nuclear membranes or in the cytoplasm.
- **G protein linked receptors** are transmembrane receptors. They function as molecular switches to regulate enzymes, ion channels and other organelles. When a **ligand** activates (turns "on") the G protein receptor it causes a conformational change that allows the receptor exchange GDP for GTP. This often triggers **signal cascades** or **second messenger pathways** to activate more G proteins.

- **Ligand gated ion channels** are regulated by ligands and are selective to ions. They are often located at synapses and aid in converting the presynaptic chemical signal from a neurotransmitter to a postsynaptic electrical signal. They are also affected by the **membrane potential** of the neuron.
- **Tyrosine kinases** are enzymes that transfer phosphates from ATP to a protein in the cell. They also act as switches and can be turned "on" or "off".

Modification of signals can cause varying cellular responses.
- If protein kinases become mutated they can cause unregulated cell growth if they are constantly in the "on" position.
- Normally, cells in the pancreas release a signal (insulin) that causes your liver, muscles and fat cells to store glucose. If the pancreatic cells that produce insulin do not work correctly, sugar can accumulate in the blood and lead to Diabetes with complications from kidney failure, blindness and heart disease.
- In multiple sclerosis, the protective layer around nerve cells is destroyed. The affected nerve cells can no longer transmit signals and this can cause muscle weakness, vision difficulties, and uncontrolled movements.
- Strokes often cause dying brain cells to release large amounts of glutamate which can kill cells that were not affected by the initial blockage.
- Cancer starts when a cell grows and divides without a signal. Tumors form because they have a blood supply due to cell communication issues.
- Neurotoxins can cause cells to undergo apoptosis and disrupt cell communication pathways.
- Anesthetics, antihistamines and birth control drugs are regulated by cellular communication signals and responses.

Can you:

☐ **explain** the difference between a secretory cell and a target cell?

☐ **discuss** how cells can communicate (three ways)?

☐ **describe** these mechanisms of communication?

☐ **identify** an example of each of these mechanisms?

☐ **describe** how plants and animals communicate differently?

☐ **describe** a signal cascade?

3. E: Transmission of information results in changes within and between biological systems.

- **Individuals can act on information and communicate it to others.**
- **Animals have nervous systems that detect external and internal signals, transmit and integrate information, and produce responses.**

Transcription factors affect gene expression.

- **Homeotic genes** are involved in developmental patterns and sequences. These genes determine what body parts are formed. An example of a homeotic gene is the *Hox* gene.
- In **embryonic induction**, one embryonic tissue influences another so that there is a unique pattern of differentiation.
- Temperature, as well as water and oxygen availability, affects seed germination in plants. **Germination** is the process where a plant emerges from a seed. Seeds often have an optimum temperature range. This range can be cool (28-40 F) or warm (76-90 F). Seeds will not germinate while **dormant** even if conditions are favorable.

Gene expression can be modified by other factors.

- **Genetic mutations** affect development in an abnormal fashion.
  - **Point mutations** exchange a single nucleotide for another.
  - **Deletions** remove one nucleotide.
  - **Insertions** add one nucleotide.
  - **Translocations** exchange nucleotides from nonhomologous chromosomes
  - **Inversions** reverse the orientation of a chromosome.
- microRNAs (miRNAs) are short nucleotide sequences that affect gene expression.
  - Found in eukaryotes
  - **Post transcriptional regulators** that target mRNAs causing the gene to be repressed or silenced

- **Apoptosis** or programmed cell death plays a role in gene expression. This is evidenced in:
  - The formation of fingers and toes requires the removal of cells between them to create space.
  - The inner lining of the uterus is sloughed off at the start of menstruation.
  - Synapses, or spaces between neurons, require that extra cells be eliminated.
  - The tail of a tadpole during metamorphosis is lost as it grows into a frog.

- Internal molecular signals in plants include **phototropism** and **photoperiodism.**
    - ○ **Phototropism** occurs when plants grow in a direction determined by light. It can also occur in fungi. Phototropism is directed by photosensitive receptors called **phototropins** and **phyto/cryptochromes**. Specific sections of plants react differently to light (e.g. stems, roots)
    - ○ **Plant hormones** are responsible for the activation of enzymes to reduce rigidity of cell walls that can cause cell walls to swell.
    - ○ **Photoperiodism** occurs when plants have seasonal changes in photoperiod to flower. This is also dependent upon photoreceptor proteins.
    - ○ **Photoperiodic plants** are classified as **long day plants** or **short day plants**. This is regulated by the hours of darkness.

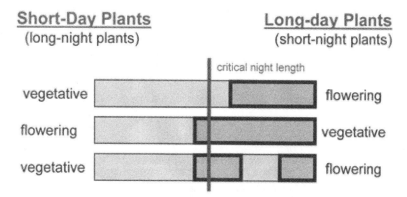

- Animals have molecular signals similar to those of plants.
    - ○ **Circadian rhythms** are 24 hour cycles. They are present in sleeping and feeding patterns, as well as to regulate body temperature, hormone production and cell regeneration. Some animals (e.g. blind rats) may show circadian rhythms in the absence of stimuli.
    - ○ Sleep wake cycles involve a group of cells in the hypothalamus of the brain. This brain tissue receives stimuli from the eyes. In response to the amount/length of day and night, the pineal gland secretes **melatonin**, a hormone. Melatonin concentrations peak at night and decrease during the day.
    - ○ Jet lag occurs when the hypothalamus cannot readjust its melatonin secretion schedule instantly. When the eyes perceive dawn or dusk earlier or later than usual, the hypothalamus may secrete too much or too little melatonin, causing jet lag.
    - ○ **Hibernation** (a state of inactivity and decreased metabolism during winter), **estivation** (a state of inactivity and decreased metabolism in summer) and **migration** (physical movement from one area to another) are all caused by biological signals.
    - ○ There are many types of **pheromones**.
        - ▪ Signal pheromones cause short term changes (e.g. neurotransmitter)
        - ▪ Primer pheromones trigger developmental events.
        - ▪ Territorial pheromones mark boundaries.

- Trail pheromones mark paths.
- Releaser pheromones cause behavioral changes.
- Alarm pheromones trigger flight and aggression.
- Fungi, protists and bacteria also have internal and external signals for regulation.
    - Fruiting bodies are produced in fungi, slime molds and bacteria as a result of **signal transduction pathways**.
        - Slime molds secrete chemicals that cause cells next to them to create a multicellular slug that can form resistant fruiting bodies.
    - Bacteria use a process called quorum sensing and produce signal molecules. Bacteria have receptors that can detect the inducer or signaling molecule. When the inducer binds to the receptor, activation occurs. When the population density of bacteria is low, the concentration of the inducer decreases and the bacteria produce little inducer. When the population density increases, more inducer is synthesized. This is an example of a **positive feedback loop**.

Can you:

☐ **identify** a homeotic gene and **discuss** its function?

☐ **describe** germination?

☐ **identify** an example of a genetic mutation and describe how it affects development?

☐ **discuss** the mechanism of post translational regulators?

☐ **explain** apoptosis and its purpose in abnormal and normal development?

☐ **discuss** the difference between long day and short day plants?

☐ **explain** how phototropisms work?

☐ **explain** the role of melatonin in sleep wake cycles?

☐ **give** an example of a pheromone induced response?

☐ **describe** a signal transduction pathway?

Multiple-Choice Questions

Each of the following questions is followed by four possible answers. Select the best answer for each question. The answers are given and explained in the teacher's manual that accompanies this book.

Cell Number	Amount of DNA in pg
1	5.00×10^{26}
2	2.45×10^{8}
3	8.41×10^{22}

Three possible cell origins
E. coli
Polyploid strawberry
Rattlesnake

1. Three cells from three different organisms were obtained. The amount of DNA from each cell was extracted and measured and recorded in the table. The three possible cell origins have been listed in the second table. After reviewing this data, decide which organism provided cell number one.

    (A) E. coli
    (B) Polyploid strawberry
    (C) Rattlesnake
    (D) There is not enough information to determine the cellular origin

2. Down syndrome affects a large number of American citizens. Down syndrome appears when an individual has an extra copy of chromosome 21— a condition called Trisomy 21. How could a mutation during meiosis cause this trisomic condition?

    (A) A piece of chromosome 21 got attached to the end of chromosome number 2
    (B) A section of the long arm of chromosome 21 is deleted and the genes in that section were lost
    (C) There was an inversion of the genes on the q arm of chromosome 21
    (D) The chromosome 21s did not separate during anaphase I or anaphase II

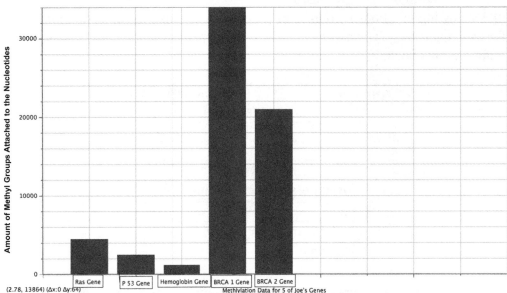

Methlylation Data for 5 genes in test subject – Joe Coogan

3. A human experimental subject—Joe Coogan had the amount of methylation present on 5 of his genes measured. The methylation data from Joe are recorded in the graph. Which one of the following statements about gene activity in Joe is an accurate conclusion from this graph?

(A) Of these five genes, Joe's BRCA 2 gene has the greatest activity.
(B) Of these five genes, Joe's BRCA 1 gene is the least active.
(C) Of these five genes, Joe's hemoglobin gene is the least active.
(D) Of these five genes, Joe's Ras gene is completely inactive.

4. Gene regulation is very important in cells. The gene regulation processes in prokaryotes are different from the gene regulation in eukaryotes. Which one of the following might be a gene regulatory process in a prokaryote?

(A) Silencing of gene by compaction as heterochromatin.
(B) Alternative splicing on introns by the spliceosome complex
(C) Inactivation of the genes that make tryptophan when a repressor binds to the operator
(D) Increasing the rate of gene activated by adding acetyl groups to the histone proteins in the chromatin

In fruit flies, long wings are dominant to vestigial wings and red eyes are dominant to brown eyes. Two flies that are heterozygous for both wing length and eye color were crossed. The phenotypes of the offspring are presented in the table.

Phenotypes of Fruit Flies	Number of Offspring Flies with that Phenotype
Long wings and red eyes	480
Long wings and brown eyes	40
Short wings and red eyes	60
Short wings and brown eyes	420

5. What inheritance pattern is seen with this data?

   (A) The data suggests that these two traits are linked on the same chromosome.
   (B) The data displays simple Mendelian inheritance.
   (C) The two alleles for wing length are codominant.
   (D) The brown eye allele appears to be located on the X chromosome.

6. Use the data in the table to calculate the cross-over frequency for these two fruit fly traits.

   (A) 0 %
   (B) 5 %
   (C) 10 %
   (D) 50 %

Hormone	Reaction Speed (milliseconds)
Insulin	2.7
Testosterone	48.2
T3	3.1
Estrogen	51.4

7. A table was given to show the reaction rates of 4 different hormones in a human subject. What information about the hormone structures can be taken from these data?

   (A) Since the reaction rates are slow for both estrogen and testosterone, they are probably steroid hormones.
   (B) Insulin is a steroid hormone made by the adrenal cortex.
   (C) T_3 and estrogen are both protein hormones.
   (D) Faster reaction rates are indicative of steroid hormones.

8. Hemophilia is a bleeding disorder that is due to a recessive X-linked allele. If Mary is heterozygous for hemophilia and Bob suffers from hemophilia, what is the probability of their daughters having hemophilia?

    (A) 0%
    (B) 25%
    (C) 50%
    (D) 100%

9. There are several enzymes involved with the DNA replication process. Why is DNA ligase involved with the production of the lagging strand of DNA but not the leading strand of DNA?

    (A) DNA ligase unzips the parental DNA double helix.
    (B) DNA ligase adds nucleotides to an exposed 3' side.
    (C) DNA ligase holds the separated single strands of DNA apart.
    (D) DNA ligase connects the Okazaki fragments together.

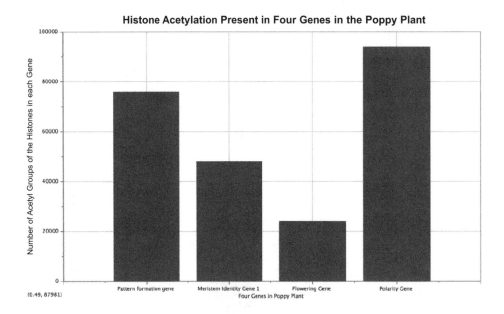

10. The graph above shows the number of acetyl groups attached to the histones of four different genes that are present in the poppy plant. Analyze this data to conclude which gene has the highest activity level.

    (A) Pattern formation gene
    (B) Meristem identity gene
    (C) Flowering gene
    (D) Polarity gene

11. In mice, the homozygous mice are black and white. The heterozygous mice are gray. What pattern of inheritance is expressed in fur color in mice?

    (A) Complete dominance and recessiveness
    (B) Codominance
    (C) Incomplete dominance
    (D) Pleiotropy

12. In pea plants, yellow peas are dominant to green peas. Smooth peas are dominant to wrinkled peas. Two plants that are heterozygous for both traits are crossed. If there are a total of 5000 offspring pea plants, what number would be expected to have green, wrinkled peas?

Grid-In Question: _____

13. This process involves using an RNA/protein complex to remove introns and connect the exons in the RNA transcript.

    (A) Proteosome digestion
    (B) Histone acetylation
    (C) DNA methylation
    (D) Alternative splicing

14. This process involves using ubiquitin as a molecular tag to be added to polypeptides that are excess or nonfunctional.

    (A) Proteosome digestion
    (B) Histone acetylation
    (C) DNA methylation
    (D) Alternative splicing

15. CH_3 functional groups are added to the nucleotides of the DNA. Which addition blocks the RNA polymerase from binding to the promoter?

    (A) Proteosome digestion
    (B) Histone acetylation
    (C) DNA methylation
    (D) Alternative splicing

16. Long distance communication is evidenced by which of the following?

   (A)   Neurons release neurotransmitters to a target cell across a synapse.
   (B)   Receptors on plant cells identify pathogens and trigger elicitors which trigger
         apoptosis in some plant cells.
   (C)   Plants secrete chemical compounds to make them less attractive.
   (D)   Insulin is secreted by the pancreas to stimulate glucose uptake in the liver.

17. Pheromones are

   (A)   chemical signals that elicit a social response.
   (B)   secreted at the synapse between neurons.
   (C)   often used as cofactors with enzymes.
   (D)   only found in eukaryotes.

18. Which of the following statements is correct regarding receptor proteins?

   (A)   There are not attachment sites for chemical messenger molecules.
   (B)   Conformational shape changes occur right before the signal molecule binds.
   (C)   Receptor proteins are not specific; they can cause shape changes in many
         proteins.
   (D)   A typical cellular response to a signal is gene regulation or enzyme activity.

19. In autocrine signaling

   (A)   cells can send intracellular signals that trigger receptors within their own
         membrane.
   (B)   gap junctions and plasmodesmata provide for metabolic cooperation between
         adjacent cells.
   (C)   recognition membrane proteins have direct contact with each other and specific
         surface molecules on plasma membranes.
   (D)   a signal molecule released by one cell that travels through the extracellular
         environment and acts on the receptor molecules of nearby cells.

20. Which of the following puts the three stages of cell signaling in the correct order?

   (A)   Reception → transduction → response
   (B)   Signal → reception → transduction
   (C)   Transduction → reception → response
   (D)   Differentiation → transduction → reception

21. In a signal transduction pathway, during transduction

    (A)   the signal molecule binds to a receptor molecule
    (B)   a secondary messenger activates a pathway to amplify the result
    (C)   a receptor molecule activates an appropriate response to the signal
    (D)   the receptor molecule undergoes a conformational shape change

22. G proteins

    (A)   bind with a receptor to trigger GTP production
    (B)   are attached to GTP in their non-active form (GDP)
    (C)   are activated for a long period of time
    (D)   can be catalyzed without the appropriate signal molecule

23. Which of the following is a result of epinephrine secretion?

    (A)   Increased insulin secretion
    (B)   Decreased heart rate
    (C)   Decreased blood flow
    (D)   Increased oxygen consumption

24. Which of the following is a mechanism for regulating signal transduction?

    (A)   The concentration of intermediate compounds affects cellular response.
    (B)   Phosphodiesterase converts AMP to cAMP to stop G-protein activity.
    (C)   Protein enzymes activate protein kinase relays.
    (D)   The rate at which signal molecules are degraded is constant

25. Which of the following describes gap junctions?

    (A)   Communicating junction between plant cells
    (B)   Anchoring junction connecting the matrix to the cytoplasm
    (C)   Communicating junction allowing passage of small molecules
    (D)   Holds cells together so materials pass through but not between the cells

26. Which of the following is an example of an intracellular receptor?

    (A)   Neuronal transmission
    (B)   Rod and cone cells in the retina
    (C)   Phosphorylation of protein kinases
    (D)   Reception of steroid hormones

27. Chemically gated ion channels function by

   (A) triggering molecular gates to open or close with transmembrane proteins
   (B) catalyzing responses intracellularly with transmembrane proteins
   (C) causing GTP to bind to G proteins and deliver the signal inside the cell
   (D) receiving signals from lipid soluble molecules with no extracellular signal
        binding sites

28. Second messengers function to

   (A) transport signals to the plasma membrane
   (B) decrease the effects of the signal molecule on the receptor
   (C) relay the message throughout the cytoplasm
   (D) convert an external signal to an internal signal

29. Which of the following is a signal molecule that binds to plasma membrane proteins?

   (A) Ligand
   (B) Second messenger
   (C) Protein kinase
   (D) Receptor protein

30. Which of the following is an example of paracrine signaling?

   (A) Response to allergens
   (B) Secretion of neurotransmitters
   (C) Secretion of epinephrine
   (D) Protein kinase secretion

Free-Response Questions for Big Idea #3

Directions: On the AP biology exam, there will be many free-response questions. These questions address a varying number of questions, and will therefore be worth a variety of points. Free-response questions may be worth between 2 - 10 points. For these questions, follow the given instructions and note the boldfaced words. Take a few minutes to brainstorm your response to the more in depth questions to organize your thoughts. Write clear complete responses in complete sentences for each question. Grading rubrics for these practice free-response questions are provided in the teacher's manual that accompanies this review book.

1. 10 points are possible on this question.

Sexual reproduction is used by many organisms as a mechanism to increase genetic variation.

(a) **Identify** and **describe** how meiosis helps contribute genetic variation in sexually reproducing organisms.

(b) **Describe** how meiosis accomplishes a reduction in chromosome number that is essential for sexual reproduction.

(c) **Compare** and **contrast** the daughter cells of meiosis to mitosis. What are the major differences between the daughter cells in meiosis and mitosis?

2. 6 points are possible on this question.

Sometimes there are errors that occur during DNA replication. If these errors are not repaired, they can alter the DNA sequence.

(a) **List** two examples of point mutation and **describe** how they can affect the protein product of that gene.

(b) **Describe** one example of phenotype that is present in one organism that is due to a point mutation.

3. 3 points are possible on this question.

There is much evidence to support the theory that the first living organisms were prokaryotes with an RNA genome. However, today, there aren't any extant organisms with an RNA genome. All the currently living organisms have a DNA genome. **Explain** how the structure of DNA would have been favored by evolution since the emergence of that first organism.

NO TESTING MATERIAL PRINTED ON THIS PAGE

GO ON TO THE NEXT PAGE

BIG IDEA!

Big Idea #4: Biological systems interact, and these interactions possess complex properties.

Key Terms for this section:

- [ ] Active site
- [ ] Alimentary canal
- [ ] Allosteric regulation
- [ ] Alveoli
- [ ] Amino acid
- [ ] Atom
- [ ] Atomic mass
- [ ] Atomic number
- [ ] Atomic weight
- [ ] Atrium
- [ ] Carbohydrates
- [ ] Cell wall
- [ ] Centriole
- [ ] Cholesterol
- [ ] Chloroplast
- [ ] Coenzymes
- [ ] Cofactors
- [ ] Competitive inhibition
- [ ] Covalent bond
- [ ] DNA
- [ ] Disaccharides

- [ ] Electrons
- [ ] Feedback inhibition
- [ ] Fatty acid
- [ ] Flame cell
- [ ] Glycolipids
- [ ] Golgi mechanism
- [ ] Heterozygous
- [ ] Homozygous
- [ ] Hormone
- [ ] Hydrogen bond
- [ ] Hydrophilic
- [ ] Hydrophobic
- [ ] Invasive species
- [ ] Ionic bond
- [ ] Isotope
- [ ] Keystone species
- [ ] Kidney
- [ ] Lysosome
- [ ] Malphigian tubule
- [ ] Mitochondrion
- [ ] Monosaccharides
- [ ] Nephridia

☐ Neuron

☐ Neurotransmitter

☐ Neutrons

☐ Niche

☐ Nonpolar covalent bond

☐ Nucleic acid

☐ Nucleolus

☐ Nucleotide

☐ Nucleus

☐ Organ

☐ Organelle

☐ Peptide bond

☐ Phagocytosis

☐ Phospholipid

☐ Plasma membrane

☐ Polar covalent bond

☐ Polysaccharides

☐ Positive feedback

☐ Protons

☐ Purine

☐ Pyrimidine

☐ RNA

☐ Radioactive isotopes

☐ Ribosome

☐ Rough endoplasmic reticulum

☐ Smooth endoplasmic reticulum

☐ Steroid

☐ Substrate

☐ Triglyceride

☐ Valence electrons

☐ Van der Waal interaction

☐ Ventricle

4. A: Interactions within biological systems lead to complex properties.

- **The subcomponents of biological molecules and their sequence determine the properties of that molecule.**
- **The structure and function of subcellular components, and their interactions, provide essential cellular responses.**
- **Interactions between external stimuli and regulated gene expression result in specialization of cells, tissues, and organs.**
- **Organisms exhibit complex properties due to interactions between their constituent parts.**
- **Communities are composed of populations of organisms that interact in complex ways.**
- **Interactions among living systems and with their environment result in the movement of matter and energy.**

The behavior of an element is determined by its atomic structure.

- The **atom** is composed of three subatomic particles: neutrally charged **neutrons** in the nucleus, positively charged **protons** in the nucleus, and negatively charged **electrons** in orbitals surrounding the nucleus.
- The mass of the atom is due to the number of protons and neutrons in the nucleus. Neutrons and protons have a mass that is several powers of 10 heavier than an electron.
- The **atomic number** is equal to the number of protons in the nucleus.
- The **atomic mass** is equal to the number of protons and the number of neutrons.
- The **atomic weight** is the weighted average of all of the isotope forms of an atom.
- Atoms of the same element can have different numbers of neutrons which gives the atom a different mass number as well. These atoms are called **isotopes**.
- **Radioactive isotopes** are actively decaying to more stable atoms. These isotopes can be used for radiometric dating of rocks and fossils and as medical markers during biological scans.

The electron configuration of atoms determines its chemical reactivity and bonding patterns.

- Electrons are located in orbitals that surround the atom's nucleus. There are a variety of orbitals shapes and patterns. Each orbital can hold two electrons.
- The orbitals are organized into **energy levels**. The first energy level has one s orbital and up to two electrons. The second and third energy levels have one s and 3 p orbitals and hold up to 8 electrons. The fourth and fifth energy levels have one s, 3 p, and 5 d orbitals and hold up to 18 electrons. The sixth and seventh energy levels have one s, 3 p, 5 d, and 7 f orbitals and can hold up to 32 electrons.
- The electrons in the outermost s and p orbitals are called the **valence electrons** and determine the chemical reactivity of an atom.

- The number of valence electrons determines how an atom will bond with another atom.
- The **octet rule** says that atoms try to complete the valence energy levels through bonding.
- Two atoms can share one, two or three pairs of electrons in a **covalent bond**. This bond is very strong.
- When two atoms have fairly similar electronegativity values, they share the electrons equally in a **nonpolar covalent bond**.
- When the two atoms sharing the electrons have unequal electronegativity values, the electrons will spend more time at one atom and will be shared unequally in a polar covalent bond.
- One atom can give one, two, or three electrons to another atom. This electron transfer causes the electron donor to become a positively charged cation and the electron acceptor to become a negatively charged anion. The oppositely charged ions are attracted by an **ionic bond**. Ionic bonds are strong in dry environments, but weak in aqueous environments.

Many whole molecules can be attracted to one another in intermolecular attractions.

- A **hydrogen bond** is a temporary interaction between two molecules that both have polar covalent bonds. The more electronegative atom will pull the electrons toward it and have a partial negative charge while the less electronegative atom will have slightly positive charge. These partial charges are temporary due to the movement of electrons. The temporary positive of one polar molecule will be attracted to the temporary negative of another polar molecule.
- **Van der Waal interactions** occur between nonpolar covalent molecules. With the movement of electrons, it is possible that at any given moment, the electrons might be more around one of the atoms giving that atom a temporary negative charge and the other a temporary positive charge. The oppositely charged areas in two nonpolar molecules are attracted to one another.

Carbon is the central atom in organic molecules.

- Since carbon has four **valence electrons**, it can be involved in 4 covalent bonds. Since covalent bonds are very strong, carbon adds a lot of strength to the center of organic molecules.
- Carbon has many different bonding angles that allow for both ring structures and straight chains.
- Carbon can bond to other carbons through single, double, and triple covalent bonds which provide several different bond angles and patterns.

Organic molecules contain several reoccurring functional groups that help determine the overall properties of those molecules.

Functional Group	Structure of Functional Group	Properties of Compounds that have the Functional Group
Hydroxyl	--OH An oxygen bonded to a hydrogen	• Compounds that have it are called alcohols • Polar due to the stronger electronegativity of the oxygen atom
Carbonyl	--CO A carbon double bonded to an oxygen atom	• Ketones have carbonyl group in middle carbon • Aldehydes have carbonyl group on one of the end carbons • Slightly polar
Carboxyl	--COOH A carbon double bonded to an oxygen atom and bonded to a hydroxyl group	• Hydrogen ions tend to dissociate giving these molecules acidic properties • Compounds that have it are called organic acids or carboxylic acids.
Amino	--NH_2 A nitrogen bonded to two hydrogen atoms	• Polar • Absorbs H+ and acts as base • Compounds that have this group are called amines
Methyl	--CH_3 A carbon bonded to three hydrogen atoms	• Compounds that have many are called hydrocarbons • Nonpolar
Phosphate	--PO_4 A phosphorous bonded to four oxygen atoms	• Very polar • Ionized • Involved in nucleotides, ATP, and phospholipids
Sulfhydryl	--SH A sulfur bonded to a hydrogen	• Compounds that have this group are called thiols • Involved in protein folding

Carbon is the central atom in all four organic macromolecules: carbohydrates, lipids, proteins, and nucleic acids.

Organic Macromolecules	Description of Structure	Functions and Examples
Carbohydrates	• Made from monomer subunits called monosaccharides. • Monosaccharides have 3 to 7 carbons and an almost equal number of oxygen atoms • Monosaccharides link together via dehydration synthesis to form a covalent bond called a glycosidic linkage • A disaccharide has two monosaccharide subunits.	• A polysaccharide has hundreds of monosaccharides subunits. • Glucose, fructose, and ribose are examples of monosaccharides • Monosaccharides and disaccharides provide energy to cells • Sucrose and lactose are common disaccharides • Polysaccharides can be used for structural support or storage of extra sugar. • Plants use starch as a storage polysaccharide and cellulose as a structural support polysaccharide • Animals and fungi use chitin as a structural support polysaccharide • Animals use glycogen as a storage polysaccharide
Lipids	• Nonpolar • Hydrophobic • Mostly hydrocarbon • Fatty acids have a carboxyl group and long hydrocarbon • Unsaturated fatty acids have multiple bonds between the carbons in the hydrocarbon • Triglycerides have a glycerol attached to three fatty acids by dehydration synthesis. • Saturated fatty acids have single bonds between the carbons in the hydrocarbon	• Triglycerides function to store energy • Phospholipids are amphipathic and important components of the cell membrane • Steroids are often hormones; their lipid structure allows them to pass through the plasma membrane and bind to a receptor on the cell's interior; estrogen and testosterone are examples of lipid hormones • Cholesterol is a steroid that is important in the cell membrane

	• Saturated fats have 2 or 3 saturated fatty acids and are solid at room temperature • Unsaturated fats have 2 or 3 unsaturated fatty acids and are liquid at room temperature • Phospholipids have a glycerol attached to two fatty acids and one phosphate group • Steroids have four fused hydrocarbon rings	
Proteins	• Monomer subunit is amino acid • Amino acid has a central carbon, a carboxyl group, an amino group, and an R group • There are 20 different amino acids and 20 different R groups • Amino acids link together by dehydration synthesis • Peptide bond is a covalent bond that forms between the carbon of the carboxyl of one amino acid and the nitrogen of the amino of the next amino acid • Proteins have very complicated 3-dimensional shape • Chaperonins organize the protein folding process • 3-dimensional shape determines the protein's function • Primary structure is the sequence of amino acids; due to peptide bonds	• Proteins have many possible functions—transport, enzymes, structural support, recognition sequences, hormones, and neurotransmitters • Function is connected to the 3-dimensional shape of the protein • When the shape of the protein is disrupted, it is denatured. • Denatured proteins are nonfunctional • Examples of proteins are collagen, rubisco, ATP synthetase, cytochrome C, catalase, hemoglobin, insulin

	• Secondary structure includes alpha helices and pleated sheet; alpha helices and pleated sheets occur because of hydrogen bonding between amino acids • Tertiary structure is the 3-dimensional shape of the protein; reinforced by attractions and bonding between R groups; bonds include disulfide bridges, hydrogen bonding, and Van der Waal interactions • Quaternary structure happens when two or more proteins come together as a large subunit protein	
Nucleic Acids	• Made up of monomer subunits called nucleotides • Nucleotides have a phosphate group, a five-carbon sugar, and a nitrogenous base • There are two possible sugars, ribose and deoxyribose • There are five possible nitrogenous bases: adenine, thymine, cytosine, guanine, and uracil. • Thymine, cytosine, and uracil have a single 6-member carbon-nitrogen ring and are called pyrimidines.	• DNA and RNA • RNA is a single strand of nucleotides • RNA has ribose sugar • RNA uses adenine, uracil, guanine, and cytosine as the nitrogenous bases • DNA is a double strand of nucleotides • DNA has deoxyribose sugar • DNA uses adenine, thymine, guanine, and cytosine as the nitrogenous bases • DNA is the genetic material • RNA can be an intermediate between DNA and proteins, can transfer amino acids, can be part of spliceosomes and ribosomes

	• Guanine and adenine have a 6-member carbon and nitrogen ring fused to a 5-member carbon-nitrogen ring and are called purines • Nucleotides link together by a phosphodiester linkage; the phosphate group of the nucleotide is attached to the sugar of the next nucleotide making a sugar-phosphate backbone	

Cell structures have specific structures and functions.

Cellular Structure	Structure of Organelle	Functions of Organelle
Plasma Membrane	• The Fluid Mosaic Model describes a phospholipid bilayer with many integral and peripheral proteins • Phosphate groups line up along aqueous interior of cell and aqueous exterior and nonpolar fatty acids are on the inside • Proteins are amphipathic • Cholesterol helps to keep space between the phospholipids and reinforces the fluidity of the membrane	• Regulates movement of materials across the cell membrane • Integral proteins act as transport vehicles • Peripheral proteins are binding sites for ligands • Membrane is lipid and hydrophobic
Nucleus	• Found in eukaryotes only • Membrane bound • Large pores in the nuclear envelope • Nucleolus in center	• Holds genetic material • Nucleolus is site of ribosomal RNA synthesis • DNA replication happens in the nucleus • Transcription of DNA happens in the nucleus

Ribosomes	• Made of ribosomal RNA • Two subunits: 30s and 70s • Two subunits sit apart and only come together during translation of mRNA into polypeptide	• Site of translation • Two subunits come together and copy mRNA into amino acid sequence
Mitochondrion	• Double phospholipid bilayer that resembles prokaryotic membrane • Inner membrane has many folds called cristae • Space in the center is called the mitochondrial matrix • Has own DNA • Has own ribosomes	• Site of cellular respiration • Mitochondrial genes are all inherited through the maternal parent • Structure is evidence of endosymbiotic theory
Chloroplast	• Only found in autotrophs • Double phospholipid bilayer that resembles prokaryotic membrane • Has own DNA • Has own ribosomes • Inner membrane is a bunch of membrane discs called thylakoids • Stack of thylakoids is called granum • Fluid-filled space around granum is the stroma	• Evidence of serial endosymbiosis • Site of photosynthesis • Light dependent reactions of photosynthesis occur in the thylakoid membranes • Light independent reactions of photosynthesis occur in the stroma
Smooth Endoplasmic Reticulum	• Only found in eukaryotes • Membranous organelle • Attached to the rough ER • Membrane exterior with inner space	• Poison detoxification of cellular compounds • Phospholipid synthesis
Rough Endoplasmic Reticulum	• Only found in eukaryotes • Membranous organelle • Attached to the smooth ER and nuclear envelope • Covered with ribosomes • Membrane exterior with inner space	• Protein folding • Membranes are synthesized in this region • Protein modification

Golgi Mechanism	• Only found in eukaryotes • Membranous organelle • Membrane exterior with inner space • Stack of membranous discs	• Have cis and trans face • Packaging of materials to be sent from the cell • Unidirectional • Materials enter the cis face and exit the trans face • Modifies lysosomes and vesicles
Lysosome	• Only found in eukaryotes • Membranous organelle • Membrane exterior with inner space • Contains hydrolytic enzymes	• Fuses with vesicles to breakdown nutrients • Breaks up nonfunctional organelles
Vacuole	• Only found in eukaryotes • Membranous organelle • Membrane exterior with inner space	• Long-term storage • Many small vacuoles in animals • One large vacuole called a tonoplast in plants
Peroxisome	• Only found in eukaryotes • Membranous organelle • Membrane exterior with inner space	• House catalase • Breaks up hydrogen peroxide that is a bi-product of metabolism
Vesicle	• Only found in eukaryotes • Membranous organelle • Membrane exterior with inner space	• Temporary storage • Size and number are maintained by the Golgi
Flagellum	• Made of nine microtubule doublets with two microtubule singles in the inside • Long protrusion from cell	• Whips back and forth to move cell • Energy dependent
Cilium	• Made of nine microtubule doublets with two microtubule singles in the inside • Short protrusion from cell	• Moves materials along the surface of cells • Numerous grouped together
Centrioles	• Only found in animals • Made up of nine microtubule triplets	• Turn into centrosomes during cell division • Help to generate the mitotic spindle during division

Cytosol	• Fluid part of cell • Mostly water	• Aqueous environment is necessary for all cells • No materials could move in or out of dry cells
Cytoskeleton	• Microtubules are large fibers; have tubulin protein • Microfilaments are fine fibers; have actin protein • Intermediate filaments are intermediate in size	• Give cell shape and support • Anchors organelles in place • Provides a foundation for some organelles to move on top of • Cytoplasmic streaming
Intercellular Junctions	• Plasmodesmata in plants • Plasmodesmata are large protein channels • Gap junctions, Desmosomes, and Tight junctions in animals • Gap junctions are large protein channels • Desmosomes have giant anchoring proteins on inside of two cells • Tight junctions have series of tiny proteins	• Plasmodesmata and gap junctions allow materials to move between the cells • Tight junctions and desmosomes anchor cells together tightly
Extracellular Matrix	• Fluid and proteins on the outside of the cell	• Connect to the cytoskeleton on the inside of the cell • Helps to hold proteins in the membrane in place

Cell specialization is possible due to gene regulation.

- Prokaryotes regulate their genome with operons. Operons use an operator to control the gene expression.
- The **operator** is an area adjacent to the promoter on the DNA. **Repressors** can bind to the operator to regulate gene activity.
- When repressors are attached to the operator, the gene is inactive. When repressors are removed from the operator, the gene is active.
- **Repressible operons** are gene systems that are generally active and only become inactivated when a repressor binds to the operator.
- **Inducible operons** are gene systems that are generally inactive and only become active when an inducer binds to the repressor which pulls the repressor off of the operator.

- Eukaryotes have many mechanisms of gene regulation that can block transcription, translation or protein folding.
- Multicellular organisms have many cells that are all genetically identical.
- **Differential gene expression** due to gene regulation is how cells can be specialized for a different function.

Regulatory Process	Effect on Protein Synthesis	Description of Process
Chromosome Compaction	Prevents transcription	Pieces of chromatin remain compacted as heterochromatin that blocks the RNA polymerase from binding to the promoter.
DNA Methylation	Prevents transcription	Methyl groups attach to the DNA nucleotides which block the binding of the RNA polymerase to the promoter.
Histone Acetylation	Increases the rate of transcription	Acetyl groups attach to the histone proteins. The histones loosen the grip on the DNA, and the DNA uncoils even more allowing the RNA polymerase greater access to the promoter.
Control Elements	Increases or decreases the rate of transcription	These sequences on the genome near the promoter like the CAAT box or TATA box serve as places where transcription factors can bind. The binding of these proteins can increase the rate of binding between the RNA polymerase and the promoter or block the binding of the RNA polymerase to the promoter.

mRNA End Cap Removal	Prevents translation	The poly A tail can be removed from the 3' side of the mRNA or the modified guanine cap can be removed from the 5' side of the mRNA. Either cap removal will result in degradation of the mRNA by hydrolytic enzymes in the cytosol.
Alternative Splicing	Alters protein product	Spliceosomes cleave introns and fuse exons together during mRNA processing. Different regions of the RNA transcript can be cleaved as introns which will leave different exon sequences and will encode a different protein product.
Interference with Protein Folding	Prevents functional protein product from forming	Chaperonins are inhibited to block the folding of proteins and prevent a functional protein product
Protein Degradation	Removes excess or damaged proteins	Damaged, excess, or denatured proteins are tagged with ubiquitin. Then, a proteasome complex digests the ubiquitin tagged molecules

Organisms are composed of smaller subunits called cells and these cells can be combined to form higher order structures in organisms.

- The **Cell Theory** states that all living things are composed of cells and that all cells come from preexisting cells.
- All physiological processes are cellular phenomena that begin at the cellular level.
- Cells that work together as a unit are called **tissues**.
- Tissues that work together as a unit are called **organs**.
- Organs that work together are called **organ systems**.
- Organ systems work together to form an entire organism.

Organisms maintain dynamic homeostasis through the interactions of several body systems.

- **Homeostasis** is a steady environment for cells. Organisms maintain homeostasis through interactions of many body systems.
- The **hypothalamus** in animals is the organ that oversees homeostatic mechanisms. The hypothalamus is the central organ in the endocrine system and is a primary organ in the nervous system.
- The endocrine system and nervous system both regulate homeostasis.
- Most homeostatic mechanisms use **negative feedback** where as one process of compound increases, the body responds by stopping or slowing the process.
- **Positive feedback** leads to instability as the increase in an action stimulates a more rapid and more dramatic increase in that process.

The nervous system controls body functions related to homeostasis.

- **Neurons** have an **axon** that sends a signal to the target cell, a **soma** that integrates the signal, and **dendrites** that receive in coming signals.
- Other neurons, muscle cells, and gland cells can be target cells of the neurons.
- Neurons release **neurotransmitters** to control actions in target cells.

Neurotransmitter	Function of Neurotransmitter
Acetylcholine	Causes muscle contraction Slows the rate of heart contraction
Glutamate	Excitatory signal involved in long-term memory
GABA	Major inhibitory neurotransmitter
Norepinephrine	Excitatory in the autonomic nervous system
Dopamine	Affect sleep, mood, attention and learning
Serotonin	Affect sleep, mood, attention and learning
Endorphins	Natural analgesics that inhibit the pain sensation
Nitric Oxide	Causes penile erection during arousal in males
Carbon Monoxide	Regulates the release of hypothalamic hormones

Hormones are a mechanism of long-distance control of homeostasis.

- Hormones are long-distance chemical regulators. They travel through the bloodstream to reach their target cells.
- Hormones are secreted by ductless glands of the endocrine system.
- Several hormones are involved in homeostatic regulation.

Hormone	Functions
Oxytocin	Milk ejection during lactation and uterine contraction
Insulin	Reduces blood sugar by increasing rate of cellular respiration and storing sugar as glycogen in the liver
Glucagon	Raises blood sugar by decreasing rate of cellular respiration and breaking glycogen stored in the liver
Antidiuretic hormone	Increases amount of water in blood by increasing the permeability of water in the nephrons
Prolactin	Milk production in mammary glands in mammals
Follicle-stimulating hormone	Stimulates sperm and egg maturation
Luteinizing hormone	Stimulates ovulation and sperm release during ejaculation
Thyroid-stimulating hormone	Activates thyroid gland
T_3 and $T4_4$	Increases metabolic rate
Calcitonin	Lowers blood calcium levels by storing extra calcium in the bone
Parathyroid hormone	Increases blood calcium levels by extracting calcium from the bone
Epinephrine and Norepinephrine	Increases metabolic rate, raises blood glucose levels, and constricts blood vessels
Glucocorticoids	Raises blood sugar levels
Mineralocorticoids	Increases reabsorption of sodium and chloride in the nephron
Androgens	Supports male reproductive tract and responsible for secondary sex characteristics in males
Estrogens	Supports female reproductive tract and responsible for secondary sex characteristics in females
Progestins	Causes thickening of the wall of the uterus
Melatonin	Involved in responses to light an dark and can affect mood

Communities are composed of populations that interact in a variety of ways.

- **Communities** consist of all of the populations in an area at a given time.
- A **food chain** shows a one-way simple diagram of feeding relationships in the community.
- A **food web** shows all of the feeding relationships in a community. There can be multiple organisms at each trophic level and populations can feed on organisms from different trophic levels.
- The **producers** in a community are the autotrophic plants, algae, and bacteria. The producers convert the energy from the sun into sugar.
- 10% of the energy of the producers goes to the primary consumers.
- The **primary consumers** are the herbivorous animals that feed on the autotrophs.
- 10% of the energy of the primary consumers goes to the secondary consumers.
- The **secondary consumers** are carnivorous animals that eat herbivores.
- 10% of the energy of the secondary consumers goes to the tertiary consumers.
- The **tertiary consumers** are the higher order carnivores that eat the secondary consumers.
- Detritivores decompose dead organic matter.

Populations in a community have an impact on the other members of the community.

- **Mutualism** describes a relationship where both populations benefit from the relationship.
- **Commensalism** describes a relationship where one population benefits and one is unaffected by the relationship.
- **Interspecific competition** describes a relationship where both populations are negatively affected by the relationship due to the energy lost during competing.
- The **competitive exclusion** principle says that no two populations can occupy the same niche in a community. One species will always be better at the niche and will out-compete the other population.
- **Predation** describes a relationship where the predator benefits by consuming the prey species that is negatively affected.
- **Herbivory** describes a relationship where the herbivore benefits by consuming the plant species that is negatively affected.
- **Parasitism** describes a relationship where the parasite benefits by gaining nutrients from the host species that is negatively affected as the health of the host species is damaged.

Can you:

☐ **describe** the structure of an atom?

☐ **compare** and **contrast** covalent bonding and ionic bonding?

☐ **explain** the processes of hydrogen bonding and van der Waal interactions?

☐ **explain** the structure and function of a variety of carbohydrates, lipids, proteins, and nucleic acids?

☐ **identify** and **describe** the roles of each of the prominent features in a cell?

☐ **compare** and **contrast** a prokaryotic cell and a eukaryotic cell?

☐ **compare** and **contrast** all of the mechanisms for gene regulation in a prokaryote and a eukaryote?

☐ **Compare** and **contrast** positive and negative feedback?

☐ **explain** how the nervous system functions to maintain homeostasis?

☐ **explain** how the endocrine system functions to maintain homeostasis?

☐ **explain** how populations interact within a community?

☐ **Compare** and **contrast** a food chain to a food web?

☐ **explain** how energy is passed through the various trophic levels?

4.B: Competition and cooperation are important aspects of biological systems.

- **Interactions between molecules affect their structure and function.**
- **Cooperative interactions within organisms promote efficiency in the use of energy and matter.**
- **Interactions between and within populations influence patterns of species distribution and abundance.**
- **Distribution of local and global ecosystems changes over time.**

The structure of a molecule directly affects a molecule's function.

Enzymes are catalytic molecules that are used by cells to speed up chemical reactions without increasing temperature. They are highly specific and act on substrates.

- The **substrate** is the chemical reactant acted upon by the enzyme
- The **active site** of an enzyme is where substrates bind. This physical site is very specific.
- **Cofactors** are non-enzyme components such as metal ions. They are found in active sites and include essential trace minerals.
- **Coenzymes** are cofactors that are organic and include many vitamins.
- The **rate of reaction** of an enzyme catalyzed reaction is affected by temperature and pH.
- Each enzyme has an optimum pH.
- Increases in temperature increase the kinetic energy and rate of intermolecular collisions and the reaction rate.
- Extremely high temperatures can denature enzymes.
- **Competitive inhibition** occurs when an inhibitor blocks the active site.
- **Feedback inhibition** occurs when an enzyme mediated reaction is inhibited due to the presence of the product. The more product there is, the less new product that will be produced.
- **Positive feedback** occurs when one of the enzymes is responsible to generating product which increases the activity of another enzyme.
- **Allosteric inhibition** occurs when an inhibitor binds at a site other than the active site.
- Other factors can also affect the rate of reaction including, but not limited to:
  - Substrate concentration: At extremely high substrate concentrations, collisions between enzymes and substrates occur so often that as soon as one substrate molecule is broken down, another fits into the active site. The rate will plateau at very high substrate concentrations.
  - Enzyme concentration: The higher the rate of the enzyme concentration, the higher the rate of the reaction, until a certain point is reached and the enzyme molecules are saturated.
  - Presence of an inhibitor: Inhibitors can slow the rate of the reaction as they fit into the active site of the enzyme and render the enzyme unusable in terms of breaking down substrates.

Efficient functioning of organisms is often due to interactions within organisms.

Compartmentalization is a technique that organisms use to ensure that tasks are completed efficiently.

- For multicellular organisms, at the organismal level, **organs** work together in **organ** systems to complete a specific function. This collection of tissues is unique for specific organs.
  - **Exchange of gases:** The goal of respiration is to exchange gases with the environment via blood or another liquid. This exchange of gases requires a **moist membrane**.
    - **Single celled organisms** us gas exchange by simple diffusion across their membranes.
    - In plants, gases pass through pores called **stomata** in the cuticle and epidermis of the terrestrial plant. In aquatic plants, water passes through the tissues and the gases diffuse into the liquid.
    - In some simple animals, gas exchange is the same as in plants. Diffusion is the mechanism by which this occurs. Earthworms exchange oxygen and carbon dioxide through their skin. Arthropods have openings called **spiracles** that open into **trachaea**. Fish use gills for gas exchange.
    - In mammals with double circulatory systems, the **partial pressure** of oxygen in the alveolar spaces in the lungs is greater than the **partial pressure** in the blood. Due to this difference, the oxygen will diffuse into red blood cells from the air into the lungs. The partial pressure of carbon dioxide in the lungs is also less than in the blood, so the carbon dioxide diffuses out from the red blood cells and into the air in the lungs. The oxygen rich blood will be carried to the heart and then to the body. The reverse is true in the body tissues; the pressure of oxygen in the blood is higher than in the body tissues so the oxygen diffuses out from red blood cells at the body tissues, and the opposite is true for carbon dioxide.
    - The lungs of mammals are divided into millions of air sacs called **alveoli**.

  - **Circulation of fluids:** Efficient circulatory systems have a fluid to carry the materials, vessel to distribute the blood, a pump to push the blood through the system and exchange organs to carry out the exchange of gases. These organs include the lungs and intestines to add materials to the blood and the lungs and the kidneys to remove materials from the blood.

    - **Fish** have a two chambered heart. The blood enters the **atrium**, moves into the **ventricle**, passes through the **gills** where gas exchange occurs, and then passes to the rest of the body, returning to the atrium

- **Amphibians and most reptiles** have a three chambered heart where the right **atrium** receives the **deoxygenated** blood from the blood vessels, then to the **ventricle**, then to the body. However, some blood that is reentering the **left atrium** from the skin and lungs, also enters the ventricle. Therefore, the ventricle can pump to the lungs and to the body, but there is some mixing of deoxygenated (oxygen poor) and oxygenated (oxygen rich) blood.
- **Mammals** use a four chambered heart and a double circulatory system. Blood travels from the body to the right side of the heart through and atrium and ventricle completely separated by a **septum**

○ **Digestion of food:**
- **Single celled organisms** take in nutrients directly from their outside environment.
- **Intracellular digestion**, where food is taken into cells by **phagocytosis** occurs in many invertebrates. **Sac like digestive systems** are found in many organisms where there is a single opening for food intake and waste removal.
- Most vertebrates have **alimentary canals** that consist of a tube within a tube where the food enters through the mouth and wastes leave through the anus.
- The components of the human digestive system include: mouth, pharynx, esophagus, stomach, small intestine, large intestine, and anus, as well as the salivary glands, pancreas, liver and gall bladder.

○ **Excretion of wastes:**
- Excretory systems function to collect water and filter fluids, remove waste products and excrete products from the body.
- Invertebrates may use **nephridia** as their excretory organs. Within each nephridium is a **flame cell**.
- **Malphigian tubules** also use osmosis to allow body fluids to pass back into the body and empty the nitrogenous wastes into the insect's gut.
- **Vertebrates** use **kidneys** to regulate body fluid levels. The excretory system is made up of the **kidneys, ureters, bladder and urethra.** Kidneys have tiny excretory tubules called **nephrons**.

- At the cellular level, **organelles** are specialized compartments within a cell that have specific functions. They are usually separated by membranes. Each organelle completes a specific task, in a specific environment, for the cell.

Species distribution in the biosphere is impacted by interactions between and within populations

Symbiotic relationships between organisms affect how populations evolve.

- **Mutualism** describes a relationship where both populations benefit from the relationship.
- **Commensalism** describes a relationship where one population benefits and one is unaffected by the relationship.
- **Interspecific competition** describes a relationship where both populations are negatively affected by the relationship due to the energy lost during competing.
- The **competitive exclusion principle** says that no two populations can occupy the same niche in a community. One species will always be better at the niche and will out-compete the other population.
- **Predation** describes a relationship where the predator benefits by consuming the prey species that is negatively affected.
- **Herbivory** describes a relationship where the herbivore benefits by consuming the plant species that is negatively affected.
- **Parasitism** describes a relationship where the parasite benefits by gaining nutrients from the host species that is negatively affected as the health of the host species is damaged.

Predator/prey interactions affect this distribution. When one animal eats another living animal for growth and energy, predation occurs. Population dynamics refer to changes in the size of population of organisms in relation to one another. When the population of one species affects the size of another population, this is a predator-prey interaction.

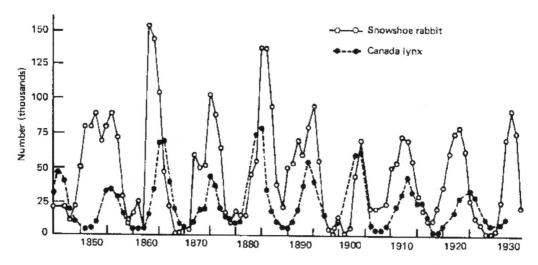

- **Invasive species** that are not native to an ecosystem can impact the dynamics of the populations in the ecosystem.

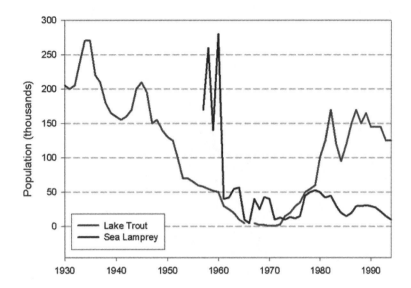

In this graph, the lake trout populations were already in decline due to overfishing and other environmental issues. At the point of the sea lamprey invasion, an invasive species, the population of lake trout was decimated. Once the sea lamprey control program was instituted, there was a quick decline of the sea lamprey population and there was recovery of the lake trout population.

- A **keystone species** is a species that has a great influence on its environment relative to its population size. It plays a crucial role in maintaining the ecosystem.
  - A common example of a keystone species is a small predator that often prevents a herbivore from eliminating a plant species. If the prey numbers are low, the keystone species population size can be low and the ecosystem will still function efficiently. Without the few predators, the herbivore population size would grow, the plants would become endangered and the ecosystem dynamics would change.

Humans often impact ecosystem dynamics and can affect species' distribution.

A **niche** describes the position of a species within its ecosystem. It often is about how a species makes its living. This could be by how it grows, limits access to other resources, what time it feeds and is active, and in general how it alters other populations.

Introduced species exploit these niches. In **niche displacement** differences among similar species whose distributions overlap geographically are exploited in regions where the species both exist.

Geologic and **meteorological** events also cause changes to these ecosystems, and specifically the niches of the organisms.

- **El Nino** is an abnormal warming of surface ocean waters. This is one part of the pattern of reversing surface air pressure in the oceans. The combination of ocean warming and pressure reversals cause El Nino.

- **Continental drift** is the movement of the Earth's continents in relation to each other.

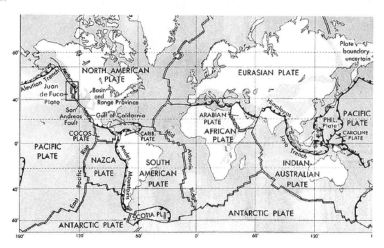

The variation exhibited by molecules allows cells to have diverse function.

Cells have very different functions due to variations in their cellular components:

- There are three different types of **lipids** in cell membranes.
  - **Phospholipids** are the most abundant lipid in the membrane. These molecules consist of two fatty acids, a phosphate group and an alcohol. The fatty acids make the molecule hydrophobic and the remainder of the molecule makes it hydrophilic.
  - The cell membrane also consists of **cholesterol**. Cholesterol is a steroid. It is absent in prokaryotes but can be found in nearly all animal membranes. It assists in maintaining fluidity of the cell membrane.
  - **Glycolipids** are also components of the cell membrane. They are composed of short chain carbohydrates and proteins and function in cell recognition.

- Different types of **hemoglobin**
  - There are three different types of normal hemoglobin. Hemoglobin A exists after birth. Hemoglobin A2 is found in red cells after birth. Hemoglobin F is the predominant hemoglobin during fetal development.
  - Different variants of hemoglobin exist in different species. This may be for an adaptive reason.

- Different types of **chlorophylls**
  - The identity, function and spectrum of the two different types of chlorophyll are very different and determined by the protein structure that surrounds them.

- Different types of **antigens**
  - **Antigens** are classified by their ability to be bound at the antigen binding site of an antibody. Antibodies are specific to the molecular structures that are present on the surface of the antigen.

The genetic makeup of an individual may affect its phenotype.

Diploid individuals have an innate functional resilience to specific issues.

- **Diploid** individuals' cells contain two sets of chromosomes. Due to the fact that there are two copies of each gene, one allele may affect the expression of the other allele.
- **Heterozygotes** are diploid individuals who possess two different alleles for a particular gene.
- **Homozygotes** are diploid individuals who possess either two of the same alleles for a particular gene.

Can you:

- ☐ **describe** the interaction between the active site of an enzyme and its substrate?

- ☐ **compare** cofactors and coenzymes and **explain** how they impact the rate of an enzymatic reaction?

- ☐ **describe** the difference between negative feedback and positive inhibition?

- ☐ **discuss** how allosteric regulation is different than competitive inhibition?

- ☐ **describe** how compartmentalization increases the efficiency of a cell and an organism?

- ☐ **describe** the different types of symbiotic relationships?

- ☐ **explain** how predator prey interactions affect the population dynamics of an ecosystem?

- ☐ **give an example** and **describe** how an invasive species can impact the dynamics of the populations in the ecosystem?

- ☐ **describe** the significance of a keystone species to an ecosystem's food web?

4.C: Naturally occurring diversity among and between components within biological systems affects interactions with the environment.

- **Variation in molecular units provides cells with a wider range of functions.**
- **Environmental factors influence the expression of the genotype in an organism.**
- **The level of variation in a population affects population dynamics.**
- **The diversity of species within an ecosystem may influence the stability.**

The environment affects the expression of traits in organisms.

The genetic makeup of an individual determines much of its structure and function, however, environmental factors also play a role in expression.

- Height and weight in humans:
- Flower color based on soil pH
- Seasonal fur color in arctic animals
- Sex determination in reptiles
- Density of plant hairs as a function of herbivory
- Effect of increased UV rays on melanin production

Organisms adapt to their local environment based upon pressures.

- As the environment has lower temperatures, darker fur in certain mammals appears.
- There are timing alterations in flowering due to climate changes

The genetic diversity of an organism directly affects its population dynamics.

If a species possesses little genetic diversity, small changes in the environmental may be extremely detrimental to its survival.

- The reaction of a population to environmental changes can be different.

If the population dynamics of one species are affected, this will impact the other species in the ecosystem.

There are critical components to the functioning of an ecosystem.

- **Keystone species** are species that have a disproportionate impact on the population in relation to the size of its population.

Can you:

☐ **predict** how species diversity influence stability within an ecosystem?

☐ **explain** how variation in molecules allows cells to have a wide range of functions?

☐ **discuss** the influence of environmental factors on phenotypes?

☐ **explain** how genotypes influence phenotypes with or without environmental influence?

☐ **describe** how responses to environmental factors result because of genotypic differences?

Multiple-Choice Questions

Each of the following questions is followed by four possible answers. Select the best answer for each question. The answers are given and explained in the teacher's manual that accompanies this book.

Javon and Kira have isolated some unicellular protist cells. They have lysed these cells, spun them on a centrifuge, and separated out some of the cellular components and biomolecules.

1. They have found an organelle that separated in the first pellet in the centrifugation and tested positive for the presence of proteins, DNA, and RNA. This structure is the _____ of the cell.

   (A) Rough endoplasmic reticulum
   (B) Smooth endoplasmic reticulum
   (C) Golgi body
   (D) Nucleus

2. They have isolated some organic molecules. One of the organic molecules that they found was a protein. All of the following characteristics are found in proteins except for

   (A) peptide bonds linking two amino acids together
   (B) purines like adenine and guanine
   (C) amino groups and carboxyl groups
   (D) alpha helices and pleated sheets in the secondary structure

3. As the smallest organelle, ribosomes were isolated in one of the last pellets. The function of the ribosomes is to

   (A) convert glucose to ATP in aerobic respiration
   (B) break up foreign molecules with hydrolytic enzymes
   (C) translate RNA into an amino acid sequence
   (D) package molecules to be sent out of the cell via exocytosis

The table gives the primary components of a eukaryotic plasma membrane and the percentage of that component in the membrane.

Plasma Membrane Component	Percentage of the membrane due to that component
Cholesterol	3.5
Oligosaccharides	8.5
Phospholipids	52.0
Peripheral Proteins	21.5
Integral Proteins	14.5

4. In the membrane component table, the cholesterol makes up only 3.5 % of the membrane. However, it has a very important function in a eukaryotic membrane as it

    (A)   adds a hydrophilic head that mixes well with the aqueous cellular interior
    (B)   reinforces the membrane fluidity by inhibiting membrane solidification
    (C)   acts as a recognition sequence for ligands to bind
    (D)   helps transport sugars across the membrane

5. The molecule that composes the greatest percentage of the membrane has

    (A)   a glycerol attached to two fatty acids and an organic phosphate group
    (B)   a series of amino acids linked by peptide bonds
    (C)   four fused hydrocarbon rings
    (D)   a string of 20-30 simple sugars linked by glycosidic linkage that forms after dehydration synthesis

The table shows the RNA products from the ras gene in a mouse. The table shows the number of base pairs for the gene sequence and 3 RNA products.

Nucleic Acid Molecule	Length of Nucleic Acid inNumber of Base Pairs
Ras gene	4,356 bp
mRNA 1	2,876 bp
pre-mRNA	4,356 bp
mRNA 2	2,490 bp

6. In this table, it is evident that the final mRNA strands are shorter than the gene sequence. Why are the mRNA strands shorter than the gene sequence?

    (A) Reverse transcriptase elongates the gene sequence following transcription.
    (B) There are non-coding introns that are removed from the mRNA sequences.
    (C) Each mRNA base pair is made from a codon of 3 DNA base pairs.
    (D) Protective end caps are added to the mRNA sequences.

7. All of the following happen to the pre-mRNA as it is converted to mRNA except for

    (A) addition of repetitive sequence of adenine nucleotides to the 3' end
    (B) addition of modified guanine to the 5' side
    (C) reverse transcriptase makes cDNA to be added to the RNA strand
    (D) non-coding introns are cleaved from the mRNA

8. What eukaryotic gene regulatory mechanism allows the formation of two final mRNA products from a single gene and single pre-mRNA transcript?

    (A) Histone acetylation
    (B) DNA methylation
    (C) Proximal control element
    (D) Alternative splicing

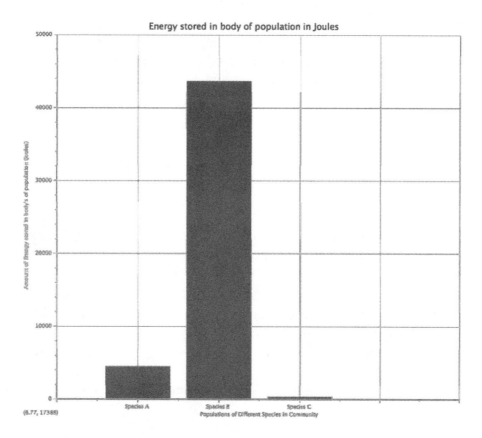

Energy stored in body of population in Joules

9. Examine the graph that depicts the amount of energy stored in the bodies of the members of three different populations in a temperate field community. From this graph, species B is probably

(A) a producer in the community
(B) a herbivore in the community
(C) a carnivore in the community
(D) a detritivore in the community

10. Examine the graph that depicts the amount of energy stored in the bodies of the members of three different populations in a temperate field community. From the graph, species C could be a(n)

(A) an oak tree population
(B) a field mouse population
(C) a black snake population
(D) a cricket population

11. Examine the graph that depicts the amount of energy stored in the bodies of the members of three different populations in a temperate field community. Use the value from the amount of energy stored in the bodies of the producer in this community to estimate a value of the amount of energy stored in the bodies of the secondary consumers.

    (A) 129 joules
    (B) 4,525 joules
    (C) 455 joules
    (D) 450,259 joules

12. Proteins experience an extensive folding process that is directed by the chaperone proteins. Which statement about the folding process is correct?

    (A) Hydrophobic R groups on amino acids will move to the protein's interior.
    (B) Positively-charged R groups on amino acids will move to other positively-charged R groups on amino acids.
    (C) Amino acids that have R groups with sulfur will hydrogen bond to each other in the protein's exterior.
    (D) Polar R groups on amino acids will interact strongly with nonpolar R groups on amino acids.

13. Epigenetics is a growing field of biology where DNA methylation patterns affect inheritance of traits. How does DNA methylation affect the activity of a gene?

    (A) It increases the rate of binding of transcription factors to control elements.
    (B) It blocks the binding of RNA polymerase to the promoter sequence.
    (C) It activates enzymes that copy the gene sequence and induce mutations.
    (D) It tags denatured proteins so that they can be digested by a proteasome complex.

14. Maria and Pedro are college students that have just isolated a molecule experimentally. What trait would they look for in this unknown molecule to find out if it is an example of an organic molecule?

    (A) They would measure the solubility of the molecule in water.
    (B) They would see if adding an ion like potassium would disrupt the structure.
    (C) They would try to see if there were two oxygen molecules held together by a double covalent bond.
    (D) They would try to see if there were 2 or more carbons linked together by covalent bonds.

15. Hydrogen bonds are very important biologically. Hydrogen bonds are intermolecular attractions that are most likely to form between

    (A) two steroid molecules
    (B) two phosphate groups in ATP
    (C) a water molecule and a glucose molecule
    (D) water molecules and NaCl

16. Which of the following factors describes an organism's habitat more than defining its niche?

    (A) Reproductive behavior
    (B) Location in the community
    (C) Nocturnal behavior
    (D) Tolerance for temperature extremes

17. Three similar species of protists coexist in the same pond. This is due most likely to the fact that they

    (A) prey on the same microorganisms
    (B) grow at the same rate
    (C) occupy different niches
    (D) crowd out other species

18. In niche displacement, if two species possess similar characteristics

    (A) they will both become extinct
    (B) they will evolve to prefer different niches
    (C) their niches will remain identical
    (D) they will begin competing with a third species

19. A keystone species

    (A) often impacts an ecosystem more than its population dictates
    (B) determines the feeding patterns of the top carnivore in the food web
    (C) needs to be an omnivore to affect the most populations
    (D) is usually a plant species

20. Invasive species can frequently go unchecked in an ecosystem because

   (A)   they are always parasitic.
   (B)   they do not have any natural predators.
   (C)   they require minimal energy from the ecosystem.
   (D)   they mutate extremely quickly.

21. Which of the following excretory organs can be found in insects?

   (A)   Kidneys
   (B)   Nephridia
   (C)   Flame cells
   (D)   Malphigian tubules

22. Which of the following organisms has a single loop circulatory system?

   (A)   Fish
   (B)   Amphibian
   (C)   Reptile
   (D)   Mammal

23. An increase in enzyme concentration will cause which of the following to occur?

   (A)   A decrease in the rate of reaction
   (B)   An increase in the rate of reaction
   (C)   The reaction rate will stay the same
   (D)   The reaction rate will increase and then plateau

24. Which of the following organisms has an alimentary canal as a digestive system?

   (A)   Jellyfish
   (B)   Earthworm
   (C)   Sponge
   (D)   Flatworm

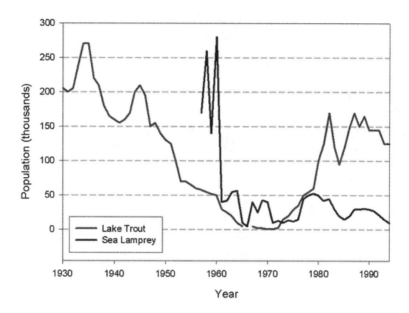

25. How many times greater is the population of Sea Lamprey than Lake Trout in 1960?

    (A)   5.5 times greater
    (B)   2.5 times greater
    (C)   3 times greater
    (D)   7 times greater

26. What is the approximate difference in the population of Lake Trout from their highest point to their lowest point?

    (A)   200,000
    (B)   300,000
    (C)   150,000
    (D)   275,000

27. What is the cause of the steep decrease in Lake Trout population in 1960?

    (A)   Natural decline brought on by an aging population
    (B)   Decreased precipitation in the Lake Superior snowbelt
    (C)   Increase in sea lamprey population
    (D)   Change in temperature of Lake Superior

28. What is the most likely reason for the decline in the sea lamprey population shortly after it reached its highest level and the lake trout population size reached its lowest level?

(A)   The sea lamprey moved to a different region of the lake.
(B)   Researchers started to remove them from the lake.
(C)   The lake trout started feeding on the sea lamprey.
(D)   Another species was introduced that preyed upon the lamprey.

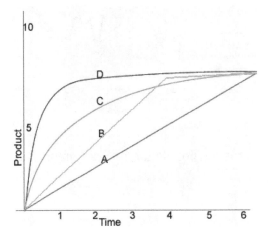

29. Which of the following is most likely due to having no enzyme present?

(A)   A
(B)   B
(C)   C
(D)   D

30. Which of the following lines represents an enzyme catalyzed reaction that is affected by a competitive inhibitor?

(A)   A
(B)   B
(C)   C
(D)   D

Free-Response Questions for Big Idea #4

Directions: On the AP biology exam, there will be 8 free-response questions. These questions address a varying number of questions, and will therefore be worth a variety of points. Free response questions will be worth between 2 - 10 points. For these questions, follow the given instructions and note the boldfaced words. Take a few minutes to brainstorm your response to the more in depth questions to organize your thoughts. Write clear complete responses in complete sentences for each question. Grading rubrics for these practice free-response questions are provided in the teacher's manual that accompanies this review book.

1.   **10 points are possible on this question.**

Cell specialization in multicellular organisms is possible through differential gene expression.

(a)   **Identify** and **describe** FOUR ways differential gene expression is possible in a eukaryotic organism.

(b)   **Compare** and **contrast** gene regulation in eukaryotes to gene regulation in prokaryotes. How can gene regulation be done by prokaryotes?

2.   **6 points are possible on this question.**

Proteins are complex molecules with very advanced folding patterns directed by the chaperone proteins.. The folding is due to the interactions between the amino acids and the R groups of the amino acids.

(a)   **Describe** THREE different kinds of R groups that might be present in a protein.

(b)   For each of those R group properties, **describe** how that property will affect the folding of the protein.

NO TESTING MATERIAL PRINTED ON THIS PAGE

GO ON TO THE NEXT PAGE

SAMPLE EXAMINATIONS

Introduction: In this section, you will be provided three complete practice exams. The answers are provided on the answer card. Detailed answer descriptions with relevant biology are given in the teacher's manual for this section. Each test has 63 multiple-choice questions, 6 grid-in questions, and 8 free-response questions. Each test will have 2 longer 10 point essays and 6 shorter essays. This format mimics the format of the AP Biology exam by the College Board.

SAMPLE EXAMINATION I

Multiple-Choice Section

Directions: In this section, select the best answer choice from the given options. These questions will stem from all areas of biology.

Plants are able to move materials through their bodies through various transport mechanisms. These questions relate to that movement through plant cells.

1. The translocation of xylem sap is

   (A) unidirectional
   (B) multidirectional
   (C) energy dependent
   (D) both a and c

2. The transport cells of the phloem are the

   (A) tracheids
   (B) vessel elements
   (C) sieve tube members
   (D) companion cells

3. Root pressure occurs when

   (A) root hairs close pores to inhibit the influx of water
   (B) water moves out of xylem and into root cells
   (C) water and minerals move into roots from soil and move into xylem tissue
   (D) phloem sap migrates into the root tissue

4. Transpiration is the

   (A) movement from a source cell to a sink cell
   (B) upward force as water and minerals move into the xylem tissue of the roots
   (C) evaporation of water through the stomata of the plant
   (D) negative pressure that blocks carbon dioxide from entering the stomata

Cells are composed of small units called biomolecules. The cell functions through the use of these small molecules.

5. A covalent bond forms when

    (A) two atoms share electrons
    (B) one atom gives one or more electrons to another
    (C) one atoms gives one or more neutrons to another
    (D) areas of partial charge attract other areas of partial charge

6. Isotopes are atoms of the same element with different

    (A) numbers of Neutrons
    (B) numbers of Electrons
    (C) numbers of Protons
    (D) both a and b

7. Sodium (Na) has one valence electron. Sodium is likely to

    (A) share electrons with another atom
    (B) accept electron(s) and become an anion
    (C) donate electron(s) and become a cation
    (D) be involved in a hydrogen bond

8. As the universal solvent, water can dissolve

    (A) polar covalent compounds
    (B) ionic compounds
    (C) nonpolar covalent compounds
    (D) both a and b

9. Carbon is the central atom in organic compounds for all of the following reasons except for

    (A) it has four covalent bonds
    (B) it can bond in a variety of angles and even rings
    (C) it can form single and multiple covalent bonds
    (D) it has a high electronegativity and adds polarity

10. The secondary structure of a protein is the

    (A) sequence of amino acids
    (B) early folding with α helix and β pleated sheet formations
    (C) overall three dimensional shape of the protein
    (D) shape after multiple protein subunits fuse together

Glycolysis is the first stage of aerobic respiration. It is the oldest energy forming process in organisms.

11. Glycolysis occurs in the

    (A) mitochondrial matrix
    (B) cristae of the inner membrane
    (C) chloroplast
    (D) cytosol

12. An aerobic process

    (A) does not occur in the presence of O_2
    (B) only occurs when O_2 is present
    (C) requires H_2O and CO_2
    (D) always occurs in the lungs in mammals

13. All of the following can occur in the absence of O_2 except for

    (A) glycolysis
    (B) oxidative phosphorylation
    (C) alcohol fermentation
    (D) lactic acid fermentation

14. Glucose is the starting material for

    (A) cellular respiration
    (B) fermentation
    (C) photosynthesis
    (D) Both a and b

This graph shows the effects of temperature on the heart rate of an aquatic organism called Daphnia magna.

15. Which statement about Daphnia magna is probably true?

    (A) It is an endothermic mammal like a rodent.
    (B) It an endothermic insect like a moth.
    (C) It is incapable of regulating its own body temperature.
    (D) It is a sessile marine organism related to the sponges.

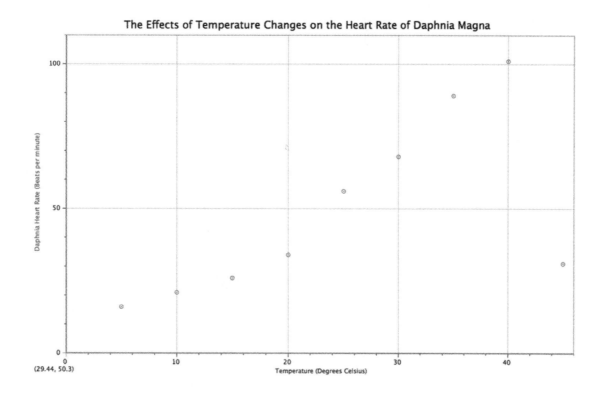

The Effects of Temperature Changes on the Heart Rate of Daphnia Magna

16. Which statement most aligns with the data in the graph about the Daphnia heart rates?

(A) Temperature and heart rate are inversely related in Daphnia magna.
(B) Temperature and heart rate are directly related in Daphnia magna.
(C) Temperature and heart rate are directly related in Daphnia magna until a certain level is exceeded.
(D) The Daphnia magna activity level is unaffected by changes in environmental temperature.

This graph shows the transpiration rates of plants at different environmental conditions. The legend on the graph gives the environmental treatment that corresponds to each data line.

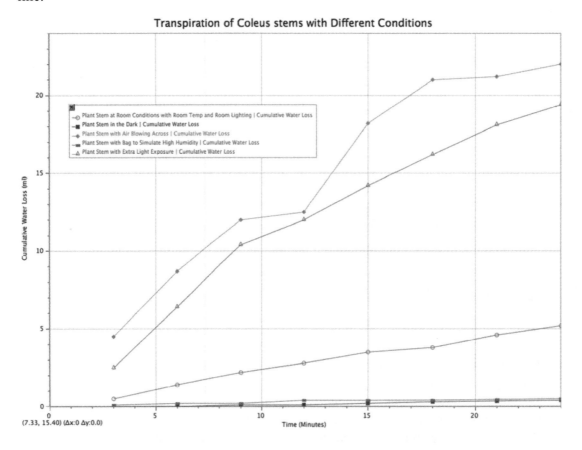

17. The water exits the plant through the stomata on the underside of the leaves. What is the most likely reason that the highest rates of transpiration were seen for the plants with air blowing across and the extra light exposure?

(A) These plants had more stomata open than the other plants.
(B) Air and light increase the amount of water that evaporates.
(C) Blowing air across the plant causes the guard cells to close over the stomata.
(D) The plant with the air blowing across the leaves has more oxygen gas available.

18. At 20 minutes, how much more water transpires from the plant with the air current compared to the plant in the humid environment?

(A) 1 time as much
(B) 5 times as much
(C) 10 times as much
(D) 50 times as much

19. Which statement about the connection between transpiration rate and photosynthetic rate is most accurate?

    (A) Plants perform more photosynthesis when the rate of transpiration is reduced.
    (B) Plants perform more photosynthesis when the rate of transpiration is increased.
    (C) The photosynthetic rate is not directly linked to the transpiration rate.
    (D) The transpiration rate is double the transpiration rate.

The table gives the percentage of genes that are active in some different cells.

Cell Type that is Being Analyzed	Percentage of Genes that Active in this Cell
E. coli—a bacterium	85%
Mesophyll Cell in a Coleus Plant	6%
Human muscle cell	3%
Human skin cell	5%
Yeast—unicellular fungus	9%

20. Why is the gene activity rate of the E. coli so much higher than the other cell types?

    (A) Prokaryotes have introns that need to be removed
    (B) Eukaryotes have many noncoding DNA sequences.
    (C) Prokaryotes have alternative splicing to follow transcription.
    (D) Eukaryotes have repressible operons to control gene activity.

21. Why is the gene activity level in the human muscle cell less than the human skin cell?

    (A) Muscle cells have more introns than skin cells.
    (B) Muscle cells have only repressible operons while skin cells have both repressible and inducible operons.
    (C) Human muscle cells are highly specialized which results in additional gene inactivation.
    (D) cDNA must be used to introduce DNA to human muscle cells.

22. DNA methylation and histone acetylation are gene regulation processes used in

    (A) only one of these cells.
    (B) two of these cells.
    (C) three of these cells.
    (D) four of these cells.

The table shows the amount of DDT in the bodies of some members of a common community.

Species in the Community	Amount of DDT in the body (ppm)
Water Concentration	0.0000003
Aquatic Insect Larvae	0.0006
Small fish	0.11
Large fish	2.1
Hawk	22.5

23. If the concentration of DDT in a body water is only 0.0000003 ppm, how can the concentration of DDT in the bodies of hawks be very dangerous at 22.5 ppm?

(A) The concentrations of toxins are magnified as they move through trophic levels.
(B) Only 10% of the energy from the aquatic insect larvae reaches the body of the hawks.
(C) Hawks have cells that are more sensitive to DDT poisoning than the small fish.
(D) The small fish have an advanced urinary system that allows for more complete filtering of large toxins.

24. Which statement about energy transfer is correct with this trophic structure?

(A) 45% of the energy from the aquatic insect larvae is available to the hawks.
(B) 1% of the energy from the small fish is available to the hawks.
(C) 0.10 % of the energy from the large fish is available to the hawks.
(D) 5% of the energy form the insects are available to the hawks.

25. Which organism would have the most abundant population?

(A) Hawk
(B) Large fish
(C) Small fish
(D) Aquatic insect larvae

26. This table does not give information about the producer in this community. Where would the algal producer fit into this trophic scheme?

(A) Before aquatic insect larvae
(B) After hawks
(C) Between aquatic insect larvae and small fish
(D) Between small fish and large fish

The following nutrient agar plats show the results of a transformation experiment. Plate 1 has E. coli growing on a nutrient-enriched agar plate. Plate 2 has E. coli that have not been altered growing on a plate with nutrient enrichment and ampicillin. Some of the bacteria were transformed with a plasmid that contains a gene for resistance to ampicillin. These transformed bacteria were put onto agar plates 3 and 4. In plate 3, there was just nutrient enrichment. In plate 4, there was nutrient enrichment and ampicillin.

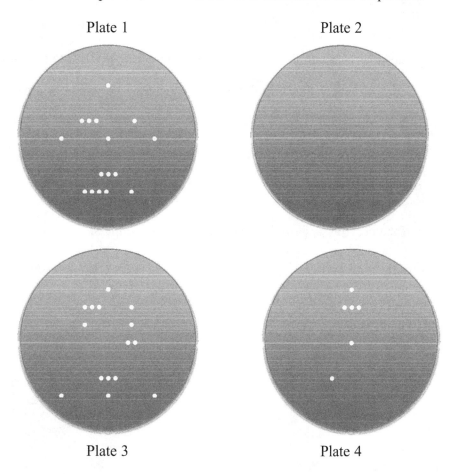

Plate 1   Plate 2

Plate 3   Plate 4

27. Why aren't any bacteria colonies growing on plate 2?

(A) The bacteria on plate 2 have been successfully transformed.
(B) Plate 2 has ampicillin which kills the unaltered bacteria.
(C) Plate 2 is missing an essential nutrient
(D) Less genes would be active on the bacteria that were introduced to plate 2.

28. Was the transformation process successful in this experiment?

(A) You cannot tell from the data.
(B) Yes, and you can tell from the growth on plate 3.
(C) Yes, and you can tell from the growth on plate 4.
(D) No, and you can tell from the lack of growth on plate 2.

29. What happens to bacteria during the transformation process?

   (A) DNA is introduced from an another bacterium through a viral intermediate.
   (B) Plasmids are passed through a pilus from one bacterial cell to another.
   (C) Random errors happen in the DNA replication process in the bacteria.
   (D) Foreign DNA binds to surface proteins on the bacteria and is brought into the bacteria' body.

The following questions relate to the coordinated actions of the vertebrate nervous system.

30. The major components of the central nervous system in a vertebrate are the

   (A) cranial nerves and spinal tracts
   (B) sensory and motor nerves
   (C) brain and the spinal cord
   (D) spinal cord and its connective tissue wrappings

31. The cells of the nervous system that are specialized for impulse conduction are the

   (A) microglia
   (B) neurons
   (C) schwann cells
   (D) oligodendrocytes

32. The receiving branches of the neuron are called the

   (A) soma
   (B) axon
   (C) dendrites
   (D) axon hillock

33. Once the neurotransmitter gets to the target cell, it

   (A) binds with receptor proteins on the surface of the target cell
   (B) passes through the cell membrane and acts on the inside of the target cell
   (C) becomes trapped in the space between the neuron and the target cell
   (D) gets converted into a new type of neurotransmitter

34. During depolarization of a neuron,

   (A) there is a rapid influx of sodium
   (B) there is a rapid efflux of sodium
   (C) there is a rapid influx of potassium
   (D) there is a rapid efflux of potassium

35. Which statement about the initiation of an impulse is true?

    (A) An impulse can have a great range of magnitudes
    (B) An impulse is an all or nothing event; it happens or it doesn't
    (C) When threshold is reached, the impulse will be blocked
    (D) A change of +10 mV from the resting state will initiate depolarization

All living organisms are composed of cells. There are two kinds of cells: prokaryotic and eukaryotic.

36. Which statement is false about a prokaryotic cell?

    (A) It has DNA as its genetic material.
    (B) It has ribosomes for protein synthesis.
    (C) It has an endoplasmic reticulum to store calcium ions.
    (D) It has a plasma membrane that is similar to the membrane structure of a chloroplast.

37. Which eukaryotic organelle is correctly matched to its function?

    (A) Mitochondrion—site of protein synthesis
    (B) Golgi mechanism—packaging of materials to be sent out of the cell
    (C) Lysosome—site of long-term storage
    (D) Nucleus—site of translation of mRNA to a protein

38. Which statement is true of animal cells but not plant cells?

    (A) During cytokinesis, a cleavage furrow forms between the two forming cells.
    (B) Several mitochondria are present for cellular respiration.
    (C) Several chloroplasts are present for photosynthesis.
    (D) There isn't any nuclear envelope present.

39. Eukaryotic cells are found in all of the following organisms except for

    (A) animals
    (B) plants
    (C) fungi
    (D) archaea

40. All of the following happen in an animal cell nucleus except for

    (A) transcription
    (B) translation
    (C) DNA replication
    (D) rRNA production

41. All of the following are common traits for kingdom Fungi except for

    (A) cell walls of chitin
    (B) decomposers
    (C) eukaryotic cells
    (D) muscles for movement

42. All of the following are common traits for Kingdom Animalia except for

    (A) cell walls of chitin
    (B) muscles for movement in most organisms
    (C) ability to move
    (D) heterotrophic

43 All of the following are common traits for Kingdom Plantae except for

    (A) autotrophic
    (B) cell walls of peptidoglycan
    (C) cell walls of cellulose
    (D) multicellular

44. The contributions of Carolus Linnaeus included

    (A) developing the binomial nomenclature
    (B) developing the first classification system
    (C) adding the domain level to the classification system
    (D) both a and b are correct

45. When an animal has only one place where it can be divided into two equal halves, it has

    (A) radial symmetry
    (B) bilateral symmetry
    (C) dueterostome development
    (D) protostome development

All living organisms perform DNA replication. It is essential to the survival of an organism.

46. The lagging strand of DNA forms during DNA replication because

(A) DNA polymerase can only move in the 3' direction
(B) DNA polymerase can only move in the 5' direction
(C) there is not enough ATP available to form two leading strands
(D) the promoter is blocked by a repressor

47. The function of the enzyme helicase it to

(A) make a new strand of DNA.
(B) hold the single strands of DNA apart so that they do not reattach.
(C) connect small DNA fragments together along the lagging strand.
(D) unwind the DNA by separating the two DNA template strands.

48. The function of the enzyme DNA ligase is to

(A) make a new strand of DNA.
(B) hold the single strands of DNA apart so that they do not reattach.
(C) connect small DNA fragments together along the lagging strand.
(D) unwind the DNA by separating the two DNA template strand.

Understanding the structure of DNA and the role of DNA as the genetic material for living cells is a major contribution to the field of molecular biology. You are presented with a set of names who have made contributions to the understanding of the structure of DNA. Select the name or name set that is responsible for the given information. The same answer can be used more than once.

49. Double helix structure of DNA.

(A) James Watson and Francis Crick
(B) Martha Hershey and Alfred Chase
(C) Frederick Griffith
(D) Maurice Wilkins and Rosalind Franklin

50. X-ray crystallography image of DNA

(A) James Watson and Francis Crick
(B) Martha Hershey and Alfred Chase
(C) Frederick Griffith
(D) Maurice Wilkins and Rosalind Franklin

51. Transformation of genetic material was possible

    (A)   James Watson and Francis Crick
    (B)   Martha Hershey and Alfred Chase
    (C)   Frederick Griffith
    (D)   Maurice Wilkins and Rosalind Franklin

52. Used radioactive sulfur and radioactive phosphorous

    (A)   James Watson and Francis Crick
    (B)   Martha Hershey and Alfred Chase
    (C)   Frederick Griffith
    (D)   Maurice Wilkins and Rosalind Franklin

53. Found that DNA caused the transformation of a bacteriophage

    (A)   James Watson and Francis Crick
    (B)   Martha Hershey and Alfred Chase
    (C)   Frederick Griffith
    (D)   Maurice Wilkins and Rosalind Franklin

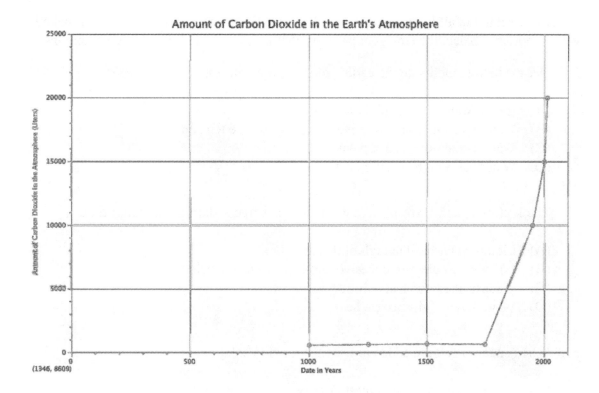

54. What happened to change the shape of this graph from flat and stable to spiking after 1800?

    (A) More animals were present on the earth.
    (B) Industrial revolution added CO_2 to the atmosphere.
    (C) The photosynthesis rate of the earth was drastically reduced.
    (D) The amount of photosynthesis and cellular respiration became evenly balanced in the ecosystem.

55. All of these factors below contribute to the currently spiking CO_2 concentrations except for

    (A) burning of fossil fuels
    (B) industry exhaust
    (C) destruction of rainforests removes autotrophs
    (D) CFCs are destroying ozone molecules

56. How does the atmospheric CO_2 concentration affect the temperature?

    (A) Temperature and CO_2 concentration are not related.
    (B) The CO_2 traps the rays from the sun at the surface of the earth.
    (C) A greater percentage of the sun's rays are reflected out into space.
    (D) The CO_2 disrupts the covalent bonds in ozone molecules.

Water is essential to all living organisms. Water has four emergent properties that make it very important. Select the emergent property that is responsible for the given situations.

57. Oceans help to moderate the earth's global temperatures.

    (A) Liquid water has the highest density.
    (B) Water molecules are cohesive and have surface tension
    (C) Water is the universal solvent.
    (D) Water has a high specific heat.

58. The bottom layer of streams and lakes does not freeze during the winter time.

    (A) Liquid water has the highest density.
    (B) Water molecules are cohesive and have surface tension.
    (C) Water is the universal solvent.
    (D) Water has a high specific heat.

59. When sugar or salt are added to water, it turns to solution.

    (A) Liquid water has the highest density.
    (B) Water molecules are cohesive and have surface tension.
    (C) Water is the universal solvent.
    (D) Water has a high specific heat.

Use the food chain to answer the questions.

Dandelion→ Cricket→Bullfrog→Eagle

60. The greatest number of organisms is found in which population?

    (A) Dandelion
    (B) Cricket
    (C) Bullfrog
    (D) Eagle

61. The smallest biomass is found in which population?

    (A) Dandelion
    (B) Cricket
    (C) Bullfrog
    (D) Eagle

62. Which population is the primary consumer?

   (A) Dandelion
   (B) Cricket
   (C) Bullfrog
   (D) Eagle

63. If a detritivore like a fungus was added to the food chain, the detritivore would feed on

   (A) One of these organisms
   (B) Two of these organisms
   (C) Three of these organisms
   (D) Four of these organisms

GRID-IN QUESTIONS

Following the multiple-choice section, there are six math-based questions where you will complete a numeric grid for the answer. You will not be given multiple-choice answers. You will calculate the answer and then bubble in the value on a scantron sheet.

In fruit flies, the wild type red eyes are dominant to the sepia eyes. This eye color trait is autosomal. In a population of 15000 fruit flies, 10000 have red eyes.

1. What is the frequency of the sepia eye allele in this population?

2. What percentage of the population of fruit flies is heterozygous for this eye color trait?

3. How many flies in the population are heterozygous for this condition?

In *Drosophila melanogaster*, the trait for sepia (brown) eyes and the trait for vestigial (short, non-functional) wings are both due to simple Mendelian inheritance. The wild type, non-mutant flies have normal wings and red eyes. The wild-type traits are dominant.

4. Two flies that are heterozygous for both traits are mated. What frequency would you expect to have red eyes and long wings and express both dominant traits?

5. If there were 500,000 offspring flies from this cross, how many would you expect to have the red eyes with the long wings?

6. You learn that the two traits are linked on the same chromosome. After the cross, you get 750 with red eyes and long wings, 47 with red eyes and vestigial wings, 68 wings with sepia eyes and long wings, and 645 with sepia eyes and vestigial wings. What is the cross-over frequency for these two traits on that chromosome?

FREE-RESPONSE SECTION

Directions: In this section, the longer questions are worth 10 points. Smaller questions can be worth 2, 3, 4 or 6 points.

1. (10 point question) Vertebrate hormones travel through the bloodstream to reach their target cells. Hormones can be a variety of kinds of molecules. Insulin is a hormone that is protein derivative and testosterone is a steroid molecule.

    a. Describe the structure of a protein hormone and give one more example.
    b. Describe the structure of a steroid hormone and give one more example.
    c. Compare and contrast the response to protein hormones and steroid hormones. Use specific hormones as examples. These hormones can be ones that are mentioned or provided or different hormones.
    d. Describe what happens on the target cell when the hormone reaches its surface.

2.   (10 point question)   The DNA sequence for a segment of a slime gene in slugs has been given.

Andalucian Slug CCGGTTACGTGCCTGACCACCCGTACGCTACGCATCGCAGACTA
Syrian Slug   CCCCTTAGCTGGCTGACCACCGGTACGCTAGGCATCGCAGACTA
Cambodian Slug CCCCTTACGTGCCTGACCACCCGTACGCTACGCATCGCAGACTA
Romanian Slug CCGATTCCGTGCCAAACCACCGGTAGGGTACGCATCGGAAACTA

Comparisons between pairs of slug species	Number of Differences Between Species	Number of Differences Between Species	Number of Differences Between Species	Number of Differences Between Species
	Andulucian	Syrian	Cambodian	Romanian
Syrian	X			
Cambodian	X	X		
Romanian	X	X	X	
Andulucian	X	X	X	X

   a.   Complete the table that shows the number of differences in this DNA sequence in the four slugs.
   b.   Draw a phylogeny that represents the evolutionary relationships of these four organisms. Be sure that phylogeny is rooted.
   c.   Which species is most closely related to the Andulucian slug? How can you determine this relationship?
   d.   Explain why DNA data is useful in making phylogenies of different organisms.

3.   (4 point question) Many living organisms can perform asexual reproduction.

   a.   Identify one organism that can perform asexual reproduction.
   b.   Describe one benefit of asexual reproduction over sexual reproduction.
   c.   Describe the asexual reproduction process that happens in the organism that was identified in part a.

4.   (4 point question) Most introduced species die in the new environment. However, some introduced species thrive in the new environment and their population climbs.

   a.   Identify one thriving introduced species and identify the affected areas.
   b.   Describe how communities can be affected by the species introduction.

5. (3 point question) Cells are able to regulate what moves across their membranes because they are selectively permeable.

    a. Describe how proteins can be used to move ions from low concentration to high across the membrane.

    b. Describe how ATP is used in this transport process.

6. (3 point question) Duchenne's muscular dystrophy is a human disorder that is due to a recessive allele on the X-chromosome. This disorder occurs almost entirely in males.

    a. Why do recessive sex-linked traits occur more frequently in males than in females?

    b. If Mary is heterozygous for this condition and Bob does not have Duchenne's muscular dystrophy, what is the probability that they will have a son with muscular dystrophy? Show work.

    c. What is the probability that they will have a daughter with muscular dystrophy? Show work.

7. (4 point question) Charles Darwin sailed on the HMS Beagle around the world. One place he stopped was the Galapagos Islands. In the Galapagos Islands, he noticed many new plant and animal species. These discoveries helped lead to writing the Origin of Species.

    a. In the Origin of Species, Darwin describes an idea called "descent with modification." What is meant by this idea?

    b. Darwin proposed evolution by natural selection as the mechanism for this descent. Explain evolution by natural selection.

8. (4 point question) Hemoglobin is a protein that is involved in transport of oxygen and carbon dioxide.

    a. Describe how the structure of a protein affects its function.

    b. Select any human protein and describe its function in a human.

NO TESTING MATERIAL PRINTED ON THIS PAGE

GO ON TO THE NEXT PAGE

SAMPLE EXAMINATION II

Multiple-Choice Section

Directions: In this section, select the best answer choice from the given options. These questions will stem from all areas of biology.

1.   Which example describes primary succession?

(A)   The reestablishment of a jack pine forest following a forest fire
(B)   The reestablishment of a herbaceous garden following a flood
(C)   The recruitment of lichens on a larval rock bed
(D)   The maturation of an herbaceous community to an arboreal community

2.   Which scenario describes secondary succession?

(A)   Grass growing in the cracks of an abandoned parking lot
(B)   The melting of winter ice makes way for spring plants to emerge
(C)   The regrowth of burned deciduous forest
(D)   The dispersal of seeds from one community to another

A team of researchers discovered a new species of organism that has prokaryotic cells, a cell wall of peptidoglycan, a hook-shaped flagellum and pili. They named the organism *Eshirichia peptidota*.

3.   Which statement is true about cell production in this organism?

(A)   The organism uses meiosis to make gametes.
(B)   The organism makes new cells regularly through mitosis and cytokinesis.
(C)   The organism only has asexual reproduction through binary fission.
(D)   The organism uses parthenogenesis as a mechanism for asexual reproduction.

4. Which statement is true about the gene regulation of this organism?

    (A) The organism has spliceosomes to do alternative splicing.
    (B) The organism uses DNA methylation to slow the inactive genes.
    (C) The organism has inducible and repressible operons for gene regulation.
    (D) The organism has histones that alter the compaction of the chromosomes.

5. Which statement is true about genetic variation that is present in this organism?

    (A) Meiosis is the major mechanism for genetic variation.
    (B) Copies of plasmids will be sent through the pili to other cells.
    (C) This organism can only perform sexual reproduction.
    (D) There is randomization in the union of the sperm and egg.

A team of researchers used a stock sucrose solution to fill 8 dialysis tubes. The 8 dialysis tubes were weighed at the beginning and then placed into 8 different solutions of known sucrose concentration. They used a solution of 0 M sucrose, 0.2 M sucrose, 0.4 M sucrose, 0.6 M sucrose, 0.8 M sucrose, 1.0 M sucrose, 1.2 M sucrose 1.4 M sucrose. They suspended one dialysis tube in each of these solutions. Then, they recorded the masses of the tubing and calculated the percent change in mass for each tube and graphed that data.

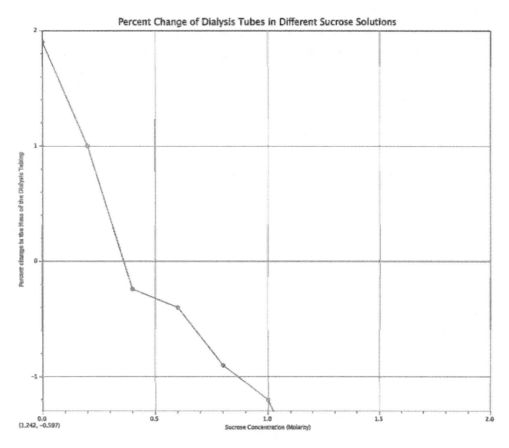

6.   Which statement best describes what happened to the dialysis tubing that was placed in 1.4 M sucrose?

(A)   The sucrose moved by active transport across the dialysis membrane.
(B)   Water moved from high water concentration to low water concentration.
(C)   Water moved by active transport with the help of a sodium-potassium pump.
(D)   The dialysis tubing ingested sucrose through phagocytosis.

7.   What value is closest to the concentration of the solution that was placed inside the dialysis tubing?

(A)   0 Molar
(B)   0.35 Molar
(C)   0.70 Molar
(D)   2.4 Molar

All living organisms undergo the same DNA replication process. There are slight differences in the process between prokaryotes and eukaryotes. Answer the questions about DNA replication about eukaryotes.

8. During DNA replication, the helicase enzyme

    (A) separates the two parental DNA strands
    (B) copies the new DNA strand
    (C) connects the fragments along the lagging strand of DNA
    (D) reconnects the DNA strands

9. During DNA replication, the DNA polymerase enzyme

    (A) separates the two parental DNA strands
    (B) copies the new DNA strand
    (C) connects the fragments along the lagging strand of DNA
    (D) reconnects the DNA strands

10. During DNA replication, the DNA ligase enzyme

    (A) separates the two parental DNA strands
    (B) copies the new DNA strand
    (C) connects the fragments along the lagging strand of DNA
    (D) reconnects the DNA strands

11. The products of DNA replication are

    (A) two identical copies of a DNA double helix
    (B) one DNA double helix and one mRNA
    (C) one mRNA and one protein|
    (D) two identical mRNA strand

12. If the parents of a cross are AaBbCc X aaBBcc, what is the probability of an offspring that is homozygous recessive for all 3 traits?

    (A) 1/64
    (B) 1/32
    (C) 1/8
    (D) 0

13. If the parents of a cross are AaBbCc X aaBBcc, what is the probability of an offspring that is heterozygous for all 3 traits?

   (A) 1/64
   (B) 1/32
   (C) 1/8
   (D) 0

14. Which statement is true about recessive sex-linked traits like colorblindness and hemophilia?

   (A) These traits occur more often in females
   (B) These traits occur with equal frequency in males and females
   (C) These traits occur more often in males
   (D) There isn't any clear trend to their frequencies of people of different genders

15. Which one of the following pairs of traits would be homologous?

   (A) Arm bones of human and wing bones of bat
   (B) Dolphin tail and swordfish tail
   (C) Bumblebee wing and blue jay wing
   (D) Gray body color in sharks and dolphins

16. Directional selection is best displayed by

   (A) white and black moths both declining while the frequency of gray moths increases
   (B) frequency of gray moths declining while frequencies of both black and white are increasing
   (C) frequency of black moths increases while white moth frequency decreases
   (D) frequencies of both black and white moths decrease

17. Individuals that are heterozygous for the sickle cell trait have a partial resistance to malaria but do not show symptoms of sickle cell. In tropical African nations, the frequency of heterozygous individuals is much, much higher than in other parts of the world. This frequency change shows

   (A) convergent evolution
   (B) directional selection
   (C) diversifying selection
   (D) stabilizing selection

18. Gene flow involves

    (A) natural disaster killing most of the members of a population
    (B) individuals moving into and out of the population
    (C) selective mating
    (D) small changes because of the environment

19. In natural selection, the selection pressures on a population are

    (A) living and nonliving features of the environment
    (B) the common ancestor between two closely related species
    (C) the hybrid offspring of a cross between two homozygous individuals
    (D) the internal cues in each member of the population

20. With natural selection, the most successful organisms

    (A) have increased muscle mass
    (B) have the most food
    (C) have an increased reproductive success
    (D) die off due to inability to evolve

This phylogeny shows the relationships between modern humans and other great ape groups.

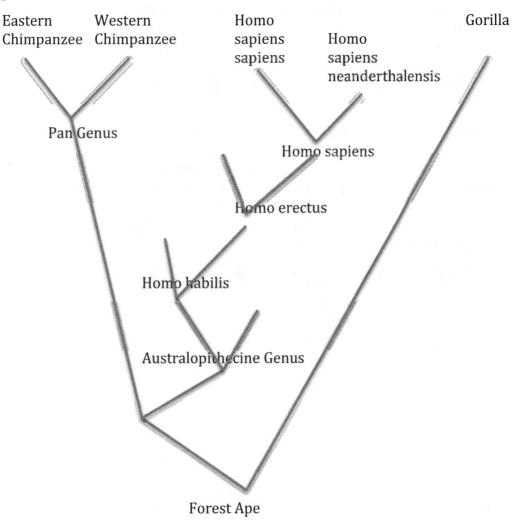

21. Which statement about these fossils is false?

(A) The Eastern chimpanzee has shared a common ancestor with modern humans more recently than it shared a common ancestor with the gorilla.
(B) The Eastern chimpanzee and the Western chimpanzee have shared a common ancestor most recently.
(C) The different Homo species have all evolved from Australopithecine ancestors.
(D) Gorillas are a common ancestor of both humans and chimpanzees.

22. Which organism is the common ancestor of chimpanzees, humans, and gorillas?

(A) Australopithecines
(B) Home habilis
(C) Pan genus
(D) Forest Ape

23. Which statement about Homo habilis is false?

    (A) Modern-day chimpanzees evolved from Homo habilis.
    (B) Homo habilis is an extinct species.
    (C) Homo habilis is a common ancestor of Homo sapiens sapiens and Homo sapiens neanderthalensis.
    (D) The Australopithecines are ancestors of Homo habilis.

A group of six AP biology students decided to do an experiment to measure the dissolved oxygen concentration of water samples from a local lake that were subjected to different light conditions to see how light exposure affects the dissolved oxygen concentration in lake water. They took 10 samples and exposed them to complete light, 90% light, 80% light, 70% light, 60% light, 50% light, 40% light, 30% light, 20% light, 10% light and darkness. After two days, the dissolved oxygen level sof the 10 water samples were taken and a graph made to represent the data.

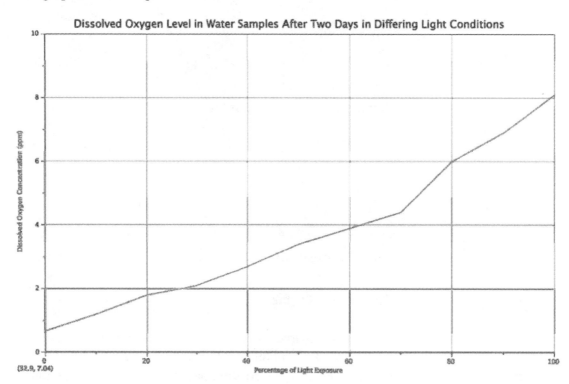

24. Why is the dissolved oxygen concentration higher at 40% light than at 0 % light?

    (A) Photosynthetic production of oxygen gas is absent in 0% light.
    (B) Heterotrophic consumers are absent in 40% light.
    (C) The amount of photosynthesis exceeds the amount of respiration in 0% light.
    (D) Decomposition is not occurring at 0% light.

25. If a water sample was subjected to 45% light, what would be the expected dissolved oxygen concentration?

   (A) 2.0 ppm
   (B) 2.5 ppm
   (C) 3.1 ppm
   (D) 6.0 ppm

In *Drosophila melanogaster*, red eyes are dominant to sepia eyes and standard wings are dominant to short vestigial wings. Female parents had red eyes and standard wings. Male parents had sepia eyes and vestigial wings. The following table shows the offspring for two generations.

Phenotype of First Offspring Flies	First Generation of Offspring (F_1 Flies)	Second Generation of Offspring Flies (F_2)
Red Eyes, Standard Wings	685	348
Red Eyes, Vestigial Wings	0	67
Sepia Eyes, Standard Wings	0	46
Sepia Eyes, Vestigial Wings	0	312

26. Explain the F_1 data that has occurred.

   (A) Sepia eye-color is located on the sex chromosome.
   (B) Sepia eyes have normal vision.
   (C) Vestigial wings are incapable of flight.
   (D) The F_1 flies are heterozygous for both traits.

27. Explain the F_2 data that has occurred.

   (A) Sepia eyes is a sex-linked trait.
   (B) Sepia eyes and vestigial wings are traits that are located on the same chromosome.
   (C) Eye color emergence is due to epistasis with the wing length gene.
   (D) There is a high mortality in wingless flies.

28. Calculate the recombination frequency between the gene for sepia eye color and vestigial wings.

    (A) 5%
    (B) 8.2%
    (C) 10.8%
    (D) 14.6%

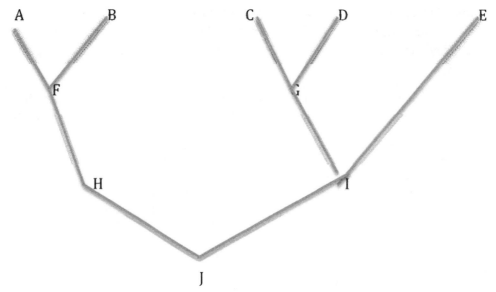

29. Which species combination is a monophyletic taxon?

    (A) Species A and B and F
    (B) Species A, B, C, D, and E
    (C) Species J, H, F, A and B
    (D) Species C, D, and E

30. Species I is the common ancestor of

    (A) C, D, E and G
    (B) A, B, C, D, and E
    (C) J and H
    (D) C and D only

31. Which species is likely to have the greatest DNA similarities with species C

    (A) A
    (B) B
    (C) D
    (D) E

Animals are multicellular organisms that have many different kinds of cells in several different body systems.

32. Which statement describes a nerve net?

   (A) Nerves that extend all over body with no centralization
   (B) Nerves with small ganglion
   (C) Nerves with brain
   (D) Nerves with brain and spinal cord

33. A cephalized animal

   (A) does not have sensory organs like a jellyfish
   (B) has sensory organs all over the body
   (C) has sensory organs in the head like a lobster
   (D) has a complete digestive tract

34. The function of the respiratory system is to

   (A) move materials throughout the body of the animal
   (B) excrete metabolic toxins
   (C) access oxygen gas and get rid of carbon dioxide
   (D) secrete hormones that regulate body processes

35. The gastrovascular cavity is used in respiration in Phylum

   (A) annelida
   (B) platyhelminthes
   (C) cnidaria
   (D) both b and c

36. Budding is an asexual reproduction mechanism that involves

   (A) eggs beginning development without being fertilized
   (B) regeneration after a body part is fragmented
   (C) a rapid series of mitosis events
   (D) a small piece drops off a parent individual and forms a clone

37. Parthenogenesis is an asexual reproduction mechanism that involves

   (A) eggs beginning development without being fertilized
   (B) regeneration after a body part is fragmented
   (C) a rapid series of mitosis events
   (D) a small piece drops off a parent individual and forms a clone

Eukaryotic organisms have many specialized cells due to differential gene expression. Many mechanisms exist in eukaryotes to regulate gene activity. Prokaryotes often exhibit gene expression.

38. Alternative splicing involves

    (A) folding of the chromatin to interfere with binding of the RNA polymerase
    (B) spliceosomes recognize different RNA regions as introns that are removed from the RNA transcript
    (C) adding a poly A tail and modified guanine cap to the RNA transcript
    (D) proteosome degradation of nonfunctioning proteins

39. DNA methylation

    (A) adds small carbon functional groups to the histone proteins
    (B) adds small carbon functional groups to the nitrogenase bases in the DNA
    (C) removes introns from the RNA transcript
    (D) degrades damaged proteins

40. The lactose operon is present in

    (A) animals only
    (B) plants only
    (C) prokaryotes only
    (D) animals and plants

41. In the lactose operon, the genes to break up lactose are usually inactive. They are only turned on when _____ is present to act as an enhancer that binds to the repressor and pulls the repressor off of the operator.

    (A) ATP
    (B) O_2
    (C) CH_4
    (D) Lactose

Living organisms live in unique ecosystems. Many of these ecosystems have similar traits that are indicative of a specific biome. Answer these questions about 4 terrestrial biomes.

42. This biome has very low rainfall and permafrost under the soil.

    (A) Desert
    (B) Tundra
    (C) Tropical Rainforest
    (D) Temperate Broadleaf Forest

43. This biome has dense vegetation and no seasonal changes

    (A) desert
    (B) tundra
    (C) tropical rainforest
    (D) temperate broadleaf forest

44. This biome has large trees as the dominant plants and mammals and birds as the dominant animal due to the seasonal changes

    (A) desert
    (B) tundra
    (C) tropical rainforest
    (D) temperate broadleaf forest

45. This biome has nocturnal animals and plants with spines as leaves due to the intense daytime heat

    (A) desert
    (B) tundra
    (C) tropical rainforest
    (D) temperate broadleaf forest

46. This biome has the greatest species diversity of any terrestrial biome.

    (A) Desert
    (B) Tundra
    (C) Tropical Rainforest
    (D) Temperate Broadleaf Forest

Maltose is a disaccharide. An enzyme called maltase helps animals digest maltose. A graph show the activity rate of the sucrose digestion at different temperatures is provided.

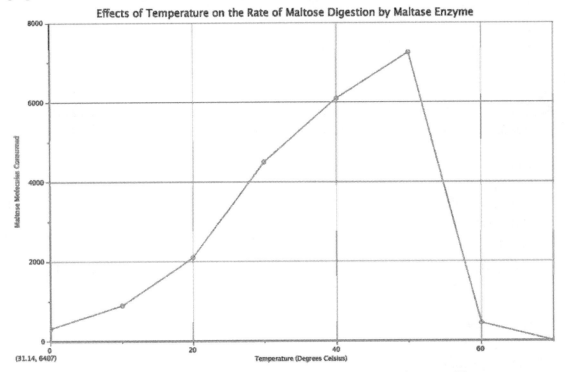

47. Why is more maltose consumed at 30 degrees C than at 10 degrees C?

    (A) An increase in temperature increases the kinetic energy of the molecules
    (B) Maltose consumption occurs in the stomach that has a temperature of 30 degrees C.
    (C) Competitive inhibitors are more abundant at lower temperatures.
    (D) Allosteric regulation is not a factor at the higher temperatures.

48. Why does the enzyme rate decline after 50 degrees Celsius?

    (A) The kinetic energy in the enzyme has reached its peak.
    (B) The hydrogen bonds in the enzyme are disrupted causing it to denature.
    (C) Competitive inhibitors are more abundant and have blocked the enzyme.
    (D) Allosteric regulation is more abundant at the higher temperatures.

49. Why does the presence of the maltase affect the breakdown of maltose?

    (A) The enzyme lowers the activation energy of the reaction.
    (B) The enzyme speeds up the rate of enzyme-catalyzed reactions.
    (C) The substrate hydrogen bonds to the enzyme and is converted to products.
    (D) All of these statements are correct.

Sympatric speciation involves the emergence of a new species from ancestral species without geographical isolation through reproductive isolation. Reproductive isolation can happen through a variety of ways.

50. In some dog breeds, the size of the reproductive anatomy is not compatible. This incompatible anatomy occurs due to

    (A) temporal isolation
    (B) habitat isolation
    (C) behavioral isolation
    (D) mechanical isolation

51. In apple maggots, some maggots feed and live on North American apple trees and some maggots feed and live on Hawthorne trees. These differential feeding patterns lead.

    (A) Temporal isolation
    (B) Habitat Isolation
    (C) Behavioral Isolation
    (D) Mechanical Isolation

52. In a blue jay species, one set of female birds only mates with males with one song while the other females mate with the males with the second mating song. This differential reproduction can lead to speciation through

    (A) temporal isolation
    (B) habitat isolation
    (C) behavioral isolation
    (D) mechanical isolation

In the Central Dogma Theory of biology, there is a connection between the DNA in cells of organisms and the proteins that are produced in the cells. During protein synthesis, there are many proteins involved in the two-step process to go from DNA to mRNA and then from mRNA to protein.

53. Which one of the following statements is correct about the role of RNA polymerase in transcription?

    (A) RNA polymerase cleaves out introns out of the primary transcript
    (B) RNA polymerase separates the two DNA strands and copies the template DNA strand into an RNA sequence
    (C) RNA polymerase brings amino acids to the ribosome
    (D) RNA polymerase builds peptide bonds between the amino acids in the forming protein.

54. How is the product of transcription in a prokaryote different from the product of transcription in a eukaryote?

    (A) The eukaryote forms an RNA transcript that needs introns removed and protective end caps added.
    (B) The prokaryote has a circular genome and makes circular mRNA.
    (C) The prokaryotic RNA fragments are much longer and require additional processing than the eukaryote.
    (D) Transcription in prokaryotes is completely unregulated; all genes are active 100% of the time.

55. In eukaryotic transcription, the role of control elements like the TATA box or the CAAT box is for

    (A) spliceosomes to attach to cleave the introns
    (B) site for the RNA polymerase to bind to transcribe the gene
    (C) they are transcribed into the start and stop codons and regulate the start and stop of translation
    (D) site for transcription factors to attach to draw the RNA polymerase to the promoter

56. Which of the following alterations to the eukaryotic genome would speed up the rate of transcription for a gene?

    (A) Methyl groups added to the nitrogenous bases of the DNA
    (B) Acetyl groups added to the histone proteins
    (C) Having the gene in a tightly compacted heterochromatin area of the Chromosome
    (D) Cleaving of introns from the RNA transcript

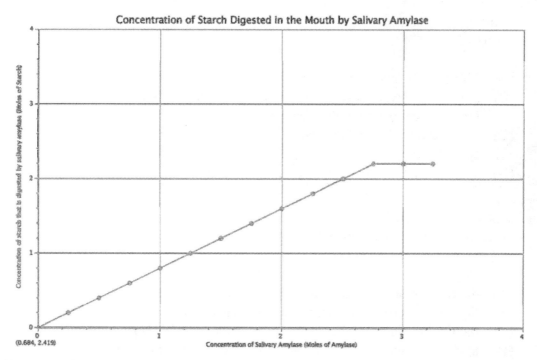

Salivary amylase is an enzyme produced by the salivary glands to digest starch in the mouth. The graph shows how the enzyme amount affects the rate of the enzyme catalyzed reaction.

57. Analyze the graph from 1.0 to 2.0 M of salivary amylase. What is the rate of the enzyme-catalyzed reaction from 1.0 M to 2.0 M salivary amylase.

    (A) 0.25
    (B) 0.40
    (C) 0.80
    (D) 1.20

58. Explain why there is steady increase in the concentration of the digested starch between 0 M salivary amylase and 2.0 M salivary amylase.

    (A) An increase in the enzyme molecule number causes an increase in the reaction product.
    (B) There are more competitive inhibitor molecules present when there are less enzyme molecules.
    (C) There was a change in the environmental pH as the enzyme concentration changed.
    (D) There was a temperature change as the enzyme concentration changed.

59. Explain what happens to the starch breakdown when the enzyme concentration exceeds 2.75 M.

    (A)   There is a plateau because all of the starch molecules are consumed.
    (B)   All of the salivary amylase molecules are active and there aren't any that remain open to bind with substrate molecules.
    (C)   The hydrogen bonds between the enzyme and substrate are altered by the environmental changes.
    (D)   The rate of the starch digestion rises exponentially.

60. When Charles Darwin visited the Galapagos Islands, he made many conclusions after observing the Galapagos finches. One conclusion that was made from those finches is

    (A)   the finches have acquired new beak shapes during their lifetimes
    (B)   these finches originated from a common ancestor
    (C)   the English finch was the common ancestor of the Galapagos finch species.
    (D)   many unrelated species that evolved without connection exist in the Galapagos Islands.

61. The extant standard sloth and the extinct giant sloth have many similarities. Why do these similarities appear according to evolution by natural selection.

    (A)   The giant sloth was the direct ancestor of the standard sloth.
    (B)   The standard sloth and the giant sloth share a common ancestor.
    (C)   The giant sloth and the standard sloth have accumulated differences due selection pressures in the environment.
    (D)   Both b and c are correct answer choices.

62. With evolution by natural selection, traits that are more favorable in the environment

    (A)   increase in frequency in the environment
    (B)   decrease in frequency in the environment
    (C)   have constant unchanging frequencies
    (D)   go extinct in the environment

63. Whales, dolphins, elephants and bats are all mammals that share a common ancestor. Which trait would have likely been present in the common ancestor of these mammals.

    (A)   wings
    (B)   flippers
    (C)   trunk-like nose
    (D)   tetrapod body structure

GRID-IN QUESTIONS

Some questions on the AP exam will have numerical answers and the numbers must be added to a grid.

Red-green colorblindness is due to a recessive sex-linked trait. Dave suffers from red-green color blindness and Mary is a carrier for red-green color blindness, but does not express the trait.

1. What percentage of their daughters are expected to be color-blind?

2. If they had 12 children, how many would be expected to be color-blind sons?

In cattle, red and white hair color are incompletely dominant. The heterozygous cattle are roan. Polled horns are dominant to long horns. A bull that is heterozygous for polled horns and roan mates with a cow that has long horns and white hair.

3. What percentage of the offspring should have roan hair and polled horns?

4. What percentage of the offspring should have white hair?

A research team went out in the field and collected 3,450 centipedes in a field with an area of 25,000 square meters. They marked these 3,450 centipedes and released them out into the field.

A week later the researchers returned to the field to collect centipedes. They collected 4,205 centipedes on the second day. 98 of the centipedes that were collected in the second week were marked from the previous capture.

The research team used the mark recapture process to estimate the size of the population were the population size.

$$N = \frac{nM}{R}$$

N = population size
n = sample size collected on day 2
M = number of individuals marked on day 1
R = number of individuals that were collected on day 2 that had marks

   5.   What is the size of the new population?

   6.   What is the density of this centipede population in this area?

FREE-RESPONSE SECTION

Directions: In this section, the longer questions are worth 10 points. Smaller questions can be worth 2, 3, 4 or 6 points.

1. (10 point question)

In a small intertidal zone on a temperate island, there are three species of mussel. Mussel 1 has lived in this region for a long time and has a tan, spiral shell. Mussel 2 has lived in this area a long time and has a gray smooth shell. Mussel 3 has been introduced in the area 10 years ago from a ship travelling to the island. The graph shows the change in population size of these three species over the past 20 years.

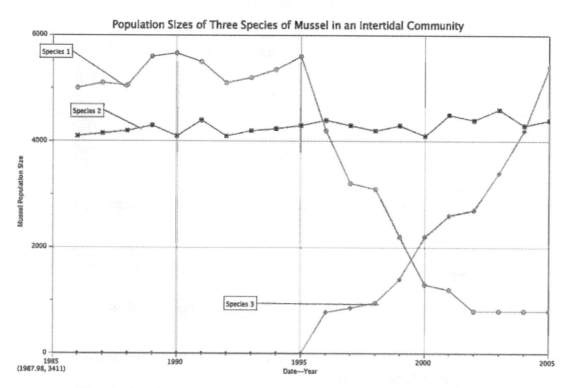

a. Explain the change in growth of each population during this period.
b. Explain how the populations of species 1 and 2 were impacted by the introduction of species 3.
c. Explain how introduced species can affect the other populations in a community.
d. Introduced species can lead to local extinctions. Describe one other process that can lead to species extinctions.

2.   (4 point question)

Water potential dramatically affects the movement of water across a cell membrane. Cell A has a higher water potential than Cell B.

     a.   What is water potential?
     b.   Will water move in or out of Cell A? Why will this movement occur?

3.   (10 point question)

Multicellular organisms like animals have many different kinds of cells. This cell variety occurs due to differential gene expression in the cell.

     a.   Select four two mechanisms of gene regulation in animals.
     b.   Explain each of those four processes and how they can lead to the differential gene expression.

4.   (2 point question)

Large mammals experience logistic population growth.

     a.   How does a carrying capacity affect that population?
     b.   Describe one trait that is present in large mammals that is common for organisms with logistic growth.

5.   (4 point question)

There are three domains of life: Archaea, Bacteria, and Eukarya. All of the organisms in these three domains have DNA as their genetic material.

     a.   Describe one characteristic about the genome of each of these that is common to organisms in all three domains.
     b.   Describe one trait that is unique to the Bacteria genome, one trait that is unique to the Archaea genome, and one trait that is unique to the eukarya genome.

6.   (4 point question)

Membranes are selectively permeable. Some molecules can cross membranes while others cannot.

   a.   Explain how an ion like calcium would be able to move across a membrane.
   b.   Explain how a steroid like cholesterol would be able to move across a membrane.

7.   (6 point question)

Water is a polar molecule.

   a.   What does it mean to be polar?
   b.   How does the polarity of water help it be a good solvent?
   c.   How does the polarity of water affect the surface tension of water?

8.   (4 point question)

Hormones are molecules that move through the bloodstream in animals to regulate body processes. These molecules tend to be protein or lipid molecules. The structure affects the way hormone binds to its target cell.

   a.   Describe 2 differences between protein hormones and lipid hormones.
   b.   Pick one human hornone and describe one target cell and its function.

NO TESTING MATERIAL PRINTED ON THIS PAGE

GO ON TO THE NEXT PAGE

SAMPLE EXAMINATION III

Multiple-Choice Section

<u>Directions</u>: In this section, select the best answer choice from the given options. These questions will stem from all areas of biology.

1. Collagen is a protein that is composed of three helical polypeptides that are wrapped around each other forming fibers. Which of the following functional roles does collagen play in the human body?

   (A) Structural tissue
   (B) Regulating body process
   (C) Immunological response to pathogens
   (D) Catalyzing metabolic reactions in cells

2. Lipids are hydrophobic molecules, that is, they do not have an attraction towards water. This is due to the covalent bonds between the hydrogen and carbon molecules. However, the nature of these bonds does affect the function of lipids. Which of the following statements regarding these bonds justifies the fact that function is different based upon the saturation of fatty acids?

   (A) The kinks in the chains do not allow the fatty acids to pack closely together
   (B) Unsaturated fatty acids yield more energy than saturated fats due to the double bonds.
   (C) Double bonds in the molecule cause them to be solid at room temperature.
   (D) Unsaturated fatty acids contain the maximum number of hydrogen atoms possible.

Phenolphthalein is an indicator that turns pink when in the presence of a base. Agar, a gelatin like substance, and phenolphthalein were mixed and formed into several sized cubes, as indicated in the table below. The cubes were soaked in a sodium hydroxide (NaOH) base until the smallest cube turned completely clear.

	Cube #1	Cube #2	Cube #3	Cube #4
Total Volume	1 cm³	8 cm³	27 cm³	64 cm³
Surface Area	6 cm³	24 cm³	54 cm³	96 cm³
Transparent Volume	0 cm³	4 cm³	12 cm³	16 cm³
Surface area to Volume Ratio	6:1	3:1	2:1	1.5:1

3. Given the data collected above, which cell had the greatest percentage of diffusion of NaOH into the agar cube?

(A) Cube 1
(B) Cube 2
(C) Cube 3
(D) Cube 4

4. Predict which of the following cubes is the most efficient in passively acquiring nutrients?

(A) Cube 1
(B) Cube 2
(C) Cube 3
(D) Cube 4

5. As cells increase in volume,

(A) the relative surface area increases
(B) the demand for material resources decreases
(C) more cellular structures are necessary for energy exchange
(D) the exchange of materials becomes more efficient

Dialysis tubing is a type of semi-permeable membrane made from cellulose. Pore size in the dialysis tubing varies. In this particular experiment, the pore size in the dialysis tubing is 20nm. Different solute molecules were placed within the dialysis tubing or in solution in the beaker. The dialysis tubing remained in the beaker for 20 minutes.

Solute Molecule	Relative Size (nm)
Chloride (Cl⁻)	0.37
Iodide (I⁻)	0.46
Glucose ($C_6H_{12}O_6$)	70
Starch ($C_{24}H_{42}O_{21}$)	209

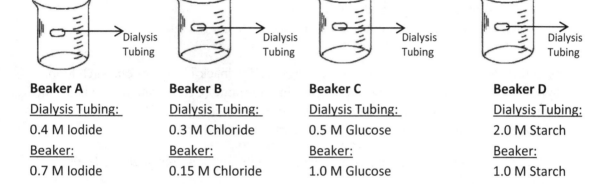

Beaker A	**Beaker B**	**Beaker C**	**Beaker D**
Dialysis Tubing:	Dialysis Tubing:	Dialysis Tubing:	Dialysis Tubing:
0.4 M Iodide	0.3 M Chloride	0.5 M Glucose	2.0 M Starch
Beaker:	Beaker:	Beaker:	Beaker:
0.7 M Iodide	0.15 M Chloride	1.0 M Glucose	1.0 M Starch

6. Predict which of the following beakers will see osmosis of water into the dialysis tubing in order to reach homeostasis?

    (A) Beaker A
    (B) Beaker B
    (C) Beaker C
    (D) Beaker D

7. Predict the concentration of glucose inside the dialysis tubing within Beaker C at the end of 20 minutes?

    (A) 0.0 M glucose
    (B) 0.5 M glucose
    (C) 0.75 M glucose
    (D) 1.0 M glucose

8.   Predict which of the following beakers will see diffusion of solutes from inside the dialysis bag out into the beaker?

   (A)   Beaker A
   (B)   Beaker B
   (C)   Beaker C
   (D)   Beaker D

9.   Which of the following statements is true regarding the relative concentrations of the dialysis tubing bags and the beakers?

   (A)   Beaker A is hypotonic to the dialysis tubing.
   (B)   Beaker B is hypertonic to the dialysis tubing.
   (C)   The dialysis tubing is isotonic to Beaker C.
   (D)   The dialysis tubing is hypertonic to Beaker D.

Many endocrine hormones are controlled by negative feedback loops. In one such loop, the hypothalamus secretes a corticotropin-releasing hormone (CRH), which stimulates the anterior pituitary gland to secrete adrenocorticotropic hormone (ACTH). ACTH stimulates the adrenal cortex to secrete a glucocorticoid called cortisol.

10.   Which of the following claims is justifiable based upon how this negative feedback loop functions?

   (A)   A tumor found in the adrenal cortex which inhibits the production of glucocorticoids will cause a decrease in the amount of ACTH produced. (increase)
   (B)   Removal of the pituitary gland will cause a decrease in the ACTH production, therefore reducing the glucocorticoid production by the adrenal cortex.
   (C)   Abnormal secretion of glucocorticoids will cause an increased secretion of CRH by the hypothalamus. (decrease)
   (D)   Increased secretion of CRH by the hypothalamus will substantially decrease glucocorticoid production by the adrenal cortex. (increase)

11. Which of the following statements connects how organisms use negative feedback to maintain their internal environments?

  (A) Corrective mechanism activated → conditions in the body change from a set point → change detected → corrective mechanisms switched off → conditions returned to set point

  (B) Conditions in the body change from a set point → change detected → corrective mechanisms activated → conditions returned to set point → corrective mechanisms switched off

  (C) Conditions returned to set point → corrective mechanisms activated → change detected → corrective mechanisms switched off → conditions in the body change from set point

  (D) Change detected → corrective mechanisms switched off → conditions returned to set point → orrective mechanisms activated → conditions in the body change from set point

12. Nucleotides are molecules that, when joined, make up DNA and RNA molecules. Which of the following molecules is a nucleotide?

  (A)

  (B)

  (C)

  (D)

13. Cellular function is based on the number and kind of sub-cellular organelles and their interactions. If one of the organelles is non-functional it can impact the activity and interaction of the cells involved. If a cell has nonfunctional Golgi bodies, predict which of the following effects occur.

   (A)   The cell will not synthesize proteins.
   (B)   Chemiosmosis will not generate ATP.
   (C)   Proteins will not be exported from the cell.
   (D)   mRNA processing will not occur.

A spectrophotometer is used to measure the relative absorbance of light by certain substances. It measures the intensity of light as a function of wavelength. In the following experiment, researchers analyzed the absorption spectrum of chlorophyll a, a photosynthetic pigment essential for photosynthesis in eukaryotes and some prokaryotes. In a subsequent experiment, researchers evaluated the effects of Cobalt on algae. Heavy metals are prevalent in poorly regulated industrial water supplies and may alter the productivity of aquatic ecosystems. Researchers analyzed the effect of Cobalt on Chlorella pyrenoidosa, a freshwater algae; specifically the concentration of chlorophyll a and an accessory pigment, chlorophyll b. Results are as follows:

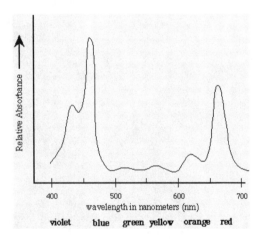

Cobalt (Co^{2+}) in parts per million (ppm)	Chlorophyll a Concentration (micrograms/ml algal suspension)	Chlorophyll b Concentration (micrograms/ml algal suspension)
0.0	8.02	7.05
0.1	8.57	7.68
0.5	10.35	9.04
1.0	6.03	5.37
2.0	4.98	4.28
3.0	4.35	3.74

Figure: The absorption spectrum of chlorophyll a. The absorbance of visible light by chlorophyll a is measured by a spectrophotometer as a function of wavelength

Data Table: Concentrations of chlorophyll found in algal suspensions after Cobalt pollution.

14. Based upon the graph, which of the following wavelengths of light (nm) has the greatest relative absorbance by chlorophyll a?

   (A)   425 nm
   (B)   550 nm
   (C)   650 nm
   (D)   675 nm

15. According to the graph, which of the following scientific questions could be posed regarding the absorbance of specific wavelengths of light by the pigment chlorophyll a?

   (A)   Why are blue and red light absorbed at the same relative levels by chlorophyll a?
   (B)   Why is the absorption of red light higher than that of blue light by chlorophyll a?
   (C)   Why does chlorophyll a not absorb green light?
   (D)   Why does yellow light have the highest relative absorption by chlorophyll a?

16. Which of the following conclusions could be reached regarding Cobalt pollution based upon the data provided?

   (A)   Low levels of Cobalt have negative effects on the rate of photosynthesis in algae.
   (B)   Both low and high levels of Cobalt have positive effects on the rate of photosynthesis in algae.
   (C)   Low levels of Cobalt have negative effects, while high levels of Cobalt have positive effects, on the rate of photosynthesis in algae.
   (D)   High levels of Cobalt have negative effects, while low levels of cobalt have positive effects, on the rate of photosynthesis in algae.

17. Which of the following predictions is possible based upon the data regarding Cobalt pollution in freshwater algae?

   (A)   At low concentrations, Cobalt inhibits the production of ATP and NADPH in the thylakoid of the chloroplast.
   (B)   At low concentrations, Cobalt stimulates the production of RuBP in the light-independent reactions of photosynthesis.
   (C)   At high concentrations, Cobalt inhibits the functioning of the electron transport chain due to an inability of the cell to produce chlorophyll.
   (D)   At high concentrations, Cobalt stimulates the production of chlorophyll a and b in the chloroplast, however, it is not able to absorb light.

Maintaining a balance between ion and water concentration inside and outside a cell is crucial in a cell. If the flow of these molecules is disrupted the consequences can be great. The Cholera toxin binds to receptors on a cell membrane. A subunit of the toxin activates the production of cAMP from ATP in the cell. The production of cAMP causes a Cl- channel in the cell to open, causing a loss of Cl- into the lumen of the small intestine. Sodium (Na+) follows the Cl-, as well as water molecules. In order to rehydrate, glucose and sodium enter the lumen in high concentrations and are moved into the cell by a glucose-sodium pump. This stimulates the movement of Cl- back into the cell, as well as water, rehydrating the cell and restoring blood volume.

18. Which of the following steps in this sequence is an example of active transport?

    (A) The loss of Cl- into the lumen of the small intestine
    (B) The movement of Na+ into the small intestine
    (C) The movement of glucose and Na+ into the cell
    (D) The movement of Cl- into the cell

19. Which of the following statements explains why water follows the movement of Na+ and Cl- into the lumen of the small intestine?

    (A) The lumen has a higher water potential than the cells.
    (B) The solute potential of the lumen becomes more negative.
    (C) The water potential of the cell is lower than that of the lumen.
    (D) The pressure potential of the lumen increases.

20. Predict which of the following causes of death is most likely if the Cholera infection is not treated.

    (A) Severe dehydration due to the immense amounts of water lost from the cells to the lumen of the small intestine
    (B) Inability of cardiac muscle to contract due to the lack of Na+ available to propagate action potentials.
    (C) Decreased production of necessary proteins in the cells due to a lack of Cl- ions.
    (D) Stroke due to the increased blood volume from the movement of water into the cells.

21. Which of the following series of events best describes the eukaryotic cell cycle?

    (A) The cell grows, doubles its DNA, prepares for cell division, and divides its chromosomes and cytoplasm.
    (B) The cell grows, divides its DNA in half, prepares for cell division and divides its chromosomes.
    (C) The cell doubles its DNA, divides its DNA, doubles its organelles, divides its chromosomes and prepares for cell division.
    (D) The cell prepares for cell division, divides its chromosomes, doubles its DNA and divides its DNA.

The following graph shows the population interaction between the snowshoe rabbit and the Canada lynx between the early 1800s and mid 1900s.

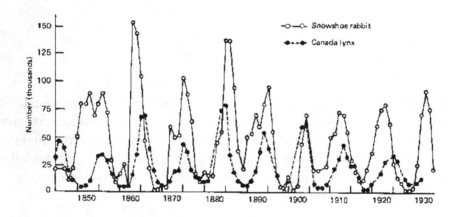

22. In the above graph, which of the following statements justifies the decrease in snowshoe rabbit population size?

    (A) The snowshoe hare population decreased due to increased predation by the Canada lynx.
    (B) The snowshoe hare population decreased due to decreased food availability.
    (C) The snowshoe hare population decreased due to decreased habitat availability.
    (D) The snowshoe hare population decreased due to increased competition for resources.

23. Predict the effect on the population dynamics of the ecosystem if the population size of mountain hare in the same habitat increased in size?

    (A) The population size of lynx would decrease due to increased competition.
    (B) The population size of snowshoe hare would decrease due to increased predation.
    (C) The population size of mountain hare would decrease due to increased competition.
    (D) The population size of snowshoe hare would increase due to decreased predation.

24. Taxol is often used in some types of chemotherapy to destroy cancer cells by preventing microtubules from stabilizing and depolymerizing. Which of the following scientific questions could be posed based upon this information?

    (A) Does Taxol bind to the microtubules during mitosis and prevent cell division?
    (B) How does Taxol inhibit helicase during the S phase of interphase?
    (C) Does Taxol prevent actin filaments from creating a cleavage furrow during cytokinesis?
    (D) Which organelles does Taxol inhibit the replication of in G_2 of interphase?

25. Predict what type of body cell will be most impacted by a patient receiving Taxol treatments?

    (A) Liver cells
    (B) Muscle cells
    (C) Neurons
    (D) Stomach cells

26. The temperature along the coast of Hawaii stays at about 70-80 F year round. Some of the most beautiful plants in the world grow along the coast. Researchers have asked you to genetically engineer one of these plants so that it can grow outdoors in Wisconsin. Given your knowledge of lipid bilayers of plants, which of the following modifications would correct a potential problem that the plants may face in Wisconsin, a much colder climate?

    (A) Shorten the length of the fatty acid chains to allow the cell membrane to be fluid at lower temperatures.
    (B) Decrease the amount of sterols in the cell membrane to decrease fluidity.
    (C) Increase the amount of cholesterol in the cell membrane to decrease the protein content.
    (D) Decrease the number of double bonds in the fatty acids to strengthen the membrane.

27. Amino acids are synthesized in the cell at the ribosome. Ribosomes can be either free or bound to the endoplasmic reticulum. Free ribosomes synthesize proteins for use in the cell. Bound ribosomes synthesize proteins for secretion. An amino acid has been genetically engineered to begin with a Rough Endoplasmic Reticulum (RER) signal sequence located before the localization sequence. Based on this information, which of the following proteins has been genetically engineered to be translated at the rough endoplasmic reticulum?

   (A) Insulin
   (B) Ferrodoxin
   (C) Cytochrome C
   (D) ATP synthase

28. Predict what would happen to the protein if it had not been genetically modified with a RER sequence?

   (A) The protein would not be synthesized.
   (B) The protein would be synthesized at the free ribosome.
   (C) The protein would be synthesized at the free ribosome, but shipped to the Golgi apparatus.
   (D) The protein would be synthesized at the bound ribosome, but not shipped to the endoplasmic reticulum.

Signal transduction describes the process by which extracellular signals cause intracellular responses. This is usually started by a signal molecule binding to a receptor in a target cell. Then, amplification of the original signal occurs and a specific cellular response results.

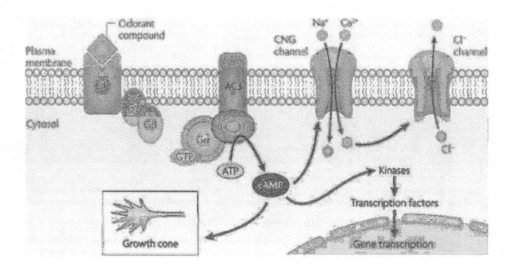

29. In the following diagram, which molecule is the signaling molecule?

    (A) Kinases
    (B) Transcription factors
    (C) Odorant compound
    (D) Na+

30. Which of the following molecules stimulates a phosphorylation cascade, amplifiying the original signal and bringing about a cellular response?

    (A) cAMP
    (B) Cl-
    (C) Transcription factors
    (D) AC3

A protozoan parasite, Plasmodium, causes a disease called malaria in humans. Chloroquine is an antimalarial drug that was once very effective against malaria. However, resistance to chloroquine has developed steadily since the 1950s.

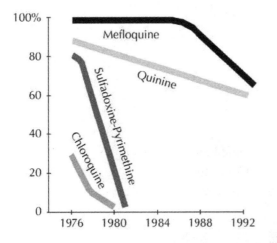

Figure 1:

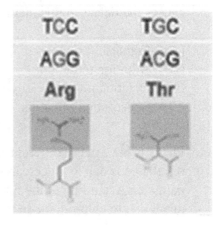

Image 1: Example of mutation in pj gene

31. Given the information above which of the following labels is correct for the y-axis on the graph?

    (A) Percent effectiveness
    (B) Percent of deaths
    (C) Percent resistant protozoans
    (D) Percent malaria cases

32. Recent studies in some African countries have revealed a significant decrease in chloroquine resistance. Which of the following questions can be posed to determine the cause for this resistance?

    (A) Does the absence of chloroquine lead to the decline in fitness of resistant protozoan species?
    (B) Does the prevalence of chloroquine resistant protozoan species affect the lifespan of mosquitoes?
    (C) Is the percent of deaths from malaria dependent upon quinine?
    (D) Does a combination of all four anti-malarial drugs impact the percent of malaria cases?

33. A gene responsible for chloroquine resistance has been designated as *pfcrt*. Several mutations in the *pfcrt* gene show correlations with the chloroquine resistance phenotype and one mutation, similar to that of the diagram, shows a perfect correlation with chloroquine resistance. Which of the following types of mutations causes the defect in this membrane transporter protein?

    (A) Frameshift mutation
    (B) Addition mutation
    (C) Deletion mutation
    (D) Substitution mutation

34. Proteins have many different functions. In the image below, chloroquine (CQ) resistance is due to a decreased accumulation of CQ in the food vacuole of the parasite. According to the image, which of the following is a plausible cause of death due to chloroquine in the parasite?

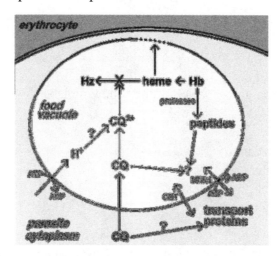

    (A) Malfunctioning transport proteins in the membrane of the vacuole
    (B) Failure to produce peptides in the vacuole
    (C) Decreased H^+ production in the vacuole
    (D) Failure to convert heme to Hz in the vacuole

35. Antibodies are produced in response to antigens. Antigens are foreign molecules that provoke this immune response. Which of the following mechanisms is not a possible mechanism for the inactivation of antigens by antibodies?

    (A) Antibodies bind to the antigen binding sites.
    (B) Antibodies tag foreign cells for destruction by phagocytosis
    (C) Antibodies reduce inflammation and production of macrophages
    (D) Antibodies enhance phagocytosis of antigens

Whooping cough is caused by a bacteria, *Bordatella pertussis*, and has symptoms that include severe coughing fits and vomiting. The following two graphs show how the rates of whooping cough have varied in the last few decades.

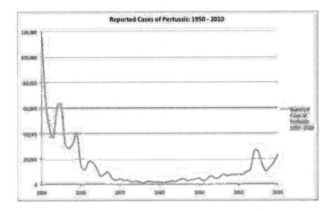
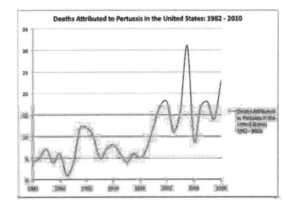

36. Approximately what percent of patients contracted a lethal case of pertussis in 2005?

    (A)   0.125%
    (B)   8.06 %
    (C)   0.253 %
    (D)   14.78 %

37. Which of the following statements is supported by the data shown above?

    (A)   The number of reported cases of pertussis rapidly declined between 2000 and 2010.
    (B)   The percent of deaths attributed to pertussis was the highest in 2005.
    (C)   The deaths attributed to pertussis decreased between 1990 and 2000.
    (D)   The highest number of reported cases of pertussis was in 2005.

38. Which of the following statements justifies the rise in reported cases of pertussis in 2005?

    (A)   Vaccination rates decreased shortly before 2005
    (B)   Autism rates increased immediately after 2005
    (C)   Antibiotic resistance of *Bordatella pertussis* decreased shortly before 2005
    (D)   Immunization rates increased shortly after 2005

The following diagram traces an action potential over time.

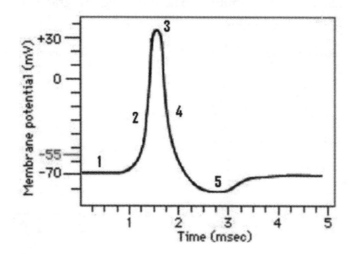

39. Which of the following stages is characterized by hyperpolarization caused by a delay in the closing of the K^+ channels?

    (A) 1
    (B) 3
    (C) 4
    (D) 5

40. Which of the following stages follows the membrane polarization due to Na+ influx?

    (A) Repolarization as Na^+ channels close and K^+ channels open
    (B) Return to resting potential
    (C) Hyperpolarization due to closing of the K^+ channels
    (D) Depolarization due to opening of the K^+ and Na^+ channels

Xyloglucan is a structural polysaccharide of plant cell walls. The enzyme xyloglucan endotransglycosylase (XET) causes the cleavage of xyloglucan, enabling cell growth. XET was isolated from germinating pea seeds and labeled with radioactive hydrogen ($^+$H). The enzyme was incubated with xyloglucan under various conditions and the concentration of the ^{3}H labeled polymer product is shown in the graph below.

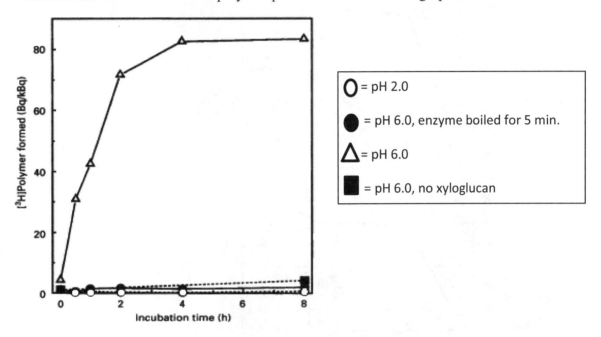

41. Xyloglucan is in a family of polysaccharides that are known to breakdown in the presence of enzymes similar to XET, but also in the presence of weak acids. Which of the trials shown on the graph ensure that the 3H labeled product formation was due to the enzymatic activity of XET alone.

(A) pH 2.0, XET
(B) pH 6.0, boiled XET
(C) pH 6.0, XET
(D) pH 6.0, no xyloglucan

42. Predict which of the following graphs would correctly represent the pH 6.0 line if additional XET were added after six hours?

(A)

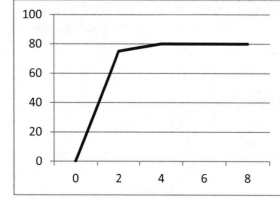

(B)

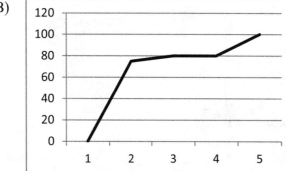

(C)

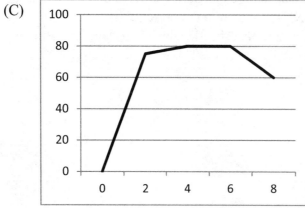

(D)

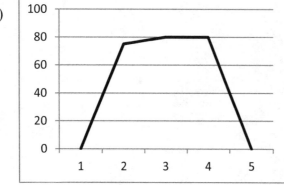

During transpiration, water passes through small pores in the leaves, called stomata, which are open to allow the passage of carbon dioxide into the plant from the outside environment and oxygen from the plant to the outside environment. This water loss is dangerous for the plant, however the stomata must be open to allow gas exchange. There are specialized cells, called guard cells, that work to regulate the opening and closing of the stomata. The following data table shows the average number of stomata per square millimeter of leaf surface area.

PLANT	UPPER EPIDERMIS	LOWER EPIDERMIS
Anacharis	0	0
Coleus	0	141
Black Walnut	0	160
Kidney Bean	40	176
Nasturtium	0	130
Sunflower	85	156
Oats	25	23
Corn	70	88
Tomato	12	130
Water Lily	460	0

43. Which of the following questions can be posed from analyzing the data above?

(A) Do all parts of the plant (leaves, stems, roots) transpire at the same rate?
(B) What environmental factors contribute to the rate of transpiration?
(C) Is there a relationship between habitat and stomata density?
(D) Does the rate of transpiration vary during different seasons?

44. Which of the following pieces of evidence best justifies the fact that environment does effect the location of stomata on a leaf?

(A) Oats and corn have the same number of stomata on the upper and lower epidermis.
(B) Anarchis does not have any stomata.
(C) The water lily has no lower epidermal stomata and the black walnut has no upper epidermal stomata.
(D) Nasturtium and coleus both lack upper epidermal stomata, but have substantial numbers of lower epidermal stomata.

45. The general equation for photosynthesis is:

$$2 \, H_2O + CO_2 + light \rightarrow carbohydrate \, (CH_2O)n + O_2 + H_2O$$

Which of the following measurements could be used to determine the rate of photosynthesis?

(A) How many moles of O_2 are produced for one mole of carbohydrate produced?
(B) How many moles of CO_2 are produced for one mole of H_2O produced?
(C) How much light is absorbed for each mole of O_2 used?
(D) How many moles of CO_2 are produced for every mole of carbohydrate used.

46. Celery stalks that are immersed in fresh water for several hours become turgid. Similar stalks left in a salt solution become flaccid. Based upon this information, we can conclude that the celery stalks are

(A) hypertonic to both fresh water and the salt solution.
(B) hypotonic to fresh water but hypertonic to the salt solution.
(C) hypotonic to both fresh water and the salt solution.
(D) hypertonic to fresh water but hypotonic to the salt solution.

Four potato cores were placed in solutions of sucrose ranging from 0M, 0.2M, 0.4M, 0.8M. The mass of the potato cores was measured at five minute increments. The following data obtained from the samples.

Potato Core Label	Sucrose Molarity (M)	Mass of Potato Cores at Each Time Interval (g)					
		Initial Mass	Time 1	Time 2	Time 3	Final Mass	
A	0M	3.0	3.5	3.8	4.4	5	.667
B	0.2M	3	3.1	3.3	3.4	3.5	.166
C	0.4M	3	2.9	2.7	2.8	2.7	-0.1
D	0.8M	3	2.1	1.9	1.6	1.3	-.567

47. Which of the following observations is supported by the data?

(A) Potato cores in the 0.8 M sucrose solution gain mass due to the influx of sugar.
(B) Potato cores in the 0.2 M sucrose solution gain mass due to the loss of starch from the potato.
(C) Potato cores in the 0 M sucrose solution gain water due to the influx of water into the potato.
(D) Potato cores in the 0.4 M lose water due to the loss of starch from the potato.

48. Which of the following processes is most likely the cause of the changes in mass observed above?

(A) Diffusion
(B) Osmosis
(C) Facilitated diffusion
(D) Active transport

49. Based upon the data above, which of the following potato cores has the greatest change in mass?

(A) Potato Core A
(B) Potato Core B
(C) Potato Core C
(D) Potato Core D

50. Which of the following statements justifies the results of the experiment above?

    (A) Water tends to move from higher concentrations of water to lower concentrations.
    (B) Sucrose moves from areas of higher concentration to areas of lower concentrations.
    (C) Water moves from areas of low water potential to high water potential.
    (D) Sucrose moves from areas of low pressure potential to high pressure potential.

51. Which of the followng statements most directly supports the claim that responses to information and communication of information are vital to natural selection?

    (A) Changes in the length of night regulate flowering and preparation for winter.
    (B) Behaviors in animals are not triggered by environmental cues.
    (C) Cooperativity between populations reduces their survival.
    (D) Changes in light sources do not affect the rate of photosynthesis in plants.

Several diseases are caused by malfunctioning organelles within cells in specific parts of the body. The diseases Tay Sachs Disease, Cystic Fibrosis and Muscular Dystrophy are three such diseases.

	Malfunction	**Populations affected**	**Signs/Symptoms**
Tay Sachs Disease	Accumulation of fat in the brain	Eastern European Jews; French Canadian	Deteriorating mental and physical abilities
Cystic Fibrosis	Thick mucous in respiratory and digestive tracts	Western European	Salty Skin; difficulty breathing, thick secretions
Muscular Dystrophy	Progressive Muscle weakness	Many	Progressive Muscle weakness

52. Tay Sachs disease is caused by an accumulation of fat in the brain. The best explanation of the occurrence of Tay Sachs disease is that the fat accumulates due to failure to produce an enzyme needed to break down specific fats by the

(A) cytoskeleton
(B) golgi apparatus
(C) lysosome
(D) peroxisome

53. Which of the following best explains the fact that individuals with cystic fibrosis are more likely to be of Western European descent?

(A) They have two genes for Cystic Fibrosis, both of which can be affected.
(B) They carry the allele for Cystic Fibrosis at a much higher rate than other ethnicities.
(C) The gene for Cystic Fibrosis mutates at a higher rate in those with Western European descent.
(D) The copy of the allele can only be affected in those with Western European descent.

Dystrophin is a protein, and a vital part of a protein complex, that connects the inner network of a muscle fiber to the surrounding extracellular matrix through the cell membrane. Normal skeletal muscle contains only small amounts of dystrophin, but the absence or the production of a less than effective protein due to a mutation in the dystrophin gene lead to harmful effects. Researchers have recently been able to substitute the missing protein with a close relative of dystrophin called utrophin. It was modified with a cell-penetrating tag, called TAT. When injected the TAT-utrophin combination spreads around the entire body and is able to penetrate the muscle cell walls.

54. Which of the following statements provides evidences as to which organelle contains the malfunctioning protein?

   (A) Cytoskeleton
   (B) Ribosome
   (C) Rough Endoplasmic Reticulum
   (D) Golgi apparatus

55. Which of the following statements best explains the mechanism by which utrophin can substitute dytstrophin in the muscle cells and not be degraded by the immune system?

   (A) Utrophin is made by every cell in the human body naturally.
   (B) Dystrophin and utrophin are molecularly identical.
   (C) The marker on the utrophin prevents it from being degraded.
   (D) Utrophin enters the muscle cells where it cannot be degraded.

The control of water concentration is one of the greatest challenges facing aquatic organisms. Freshwater species often address this challenge differently than saltwater organisms. Due to the concentration differences in their bodies relative to the environment, there is often the tendency towards a net gain or loss of water in their bodies. Freshwater species are constantly removing excess water and saltwater organisms are trying to reduce water loss. Sometimes, instead of trying to regulate their internal environments (osmoregulators) species conform to the water environment and do not control osmolarity (osmoconformers).

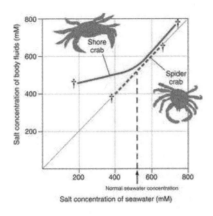

56. According to the graph, what is normal seawater concentration?

    (A) 250
    (B) 400
    (C) 525
    (D) 700

57. What is the approximate difference in salt concentration of body fluids (mM) of the two crabs at a saltwater concentration of 400 mM?

    (A) 75 mM
    (B) 100 mM
    (C) 150 mM
    (D) 200 mM

58. Which of the following hypotheses is best supported by the data collected on the graph?

   (A)   The shore crab conforms changes its habitat frequently to adapt to the changes in saltwater concentration.
   (B)   The spider crab is an osmoregulator and has the same osmolarity regardless of its environment.
   (C)   The shore crab is an osmoconformer due to the fact that it lives in a variable, brackish environment.
   (D)   The spider crab can only survive in saltwater concentrations less than 400 mM.

All organisms do not have the same oxygen carrying capacity. According to the graph the degree of oxygen saturation of hemoglobin depends on the partial pressure of oxygen.

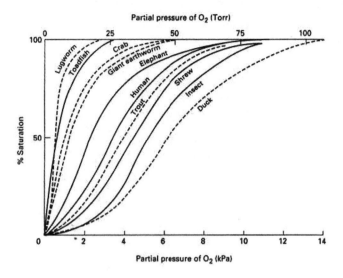

59. Which of the following scientific questions could be posed based upon the data?

    (A) Does the partial pressure of O_2 vary with temperature?
    (B) Does oxygen saturation vary between prokaryotes and eukaryotes?
    (C) Does oxygen saturation vary with the size of organisms?
    (D) Do different pigments have different oxygen capacities?

60. Which of the following organisms has a 50% Saturation of O_2 at the highest partial pressure of O_2?

    (A) Lungworm
    (B) Trout
    (C) Shrew
    (D) Insect

61. The data shown above supports the fact that

    (A) small mammals consume oxygen at higher rates than larger animals.
    (B) vertebrates have lower metabolic rates than invertebrates.
    (C) birds have the lowest affinity for oxygen.
    (D) the shrew releases oxygen more slowly than the insect.

The concentration of hemoglobin in the blood varies between different groups of humans in different environments. This is due to the fact that humans make physiological adjustments when they live in environments containing different concentrations of oxygen. Other groups of high altitude populations have inherited evolutionary adaptations for tolerance of low oxygen environments.

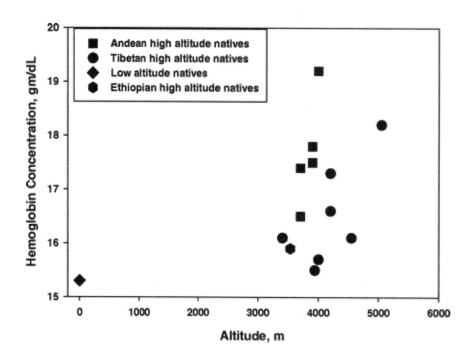

62. Which of the following populations does not appear to have an inherited evolutionary adapation while living at higher altitudes?

    (A)   Andean high altitude natives
    (B)   Tibetan high altitude natives
    (C)   Low altitude natives
    (D)   Ethiopian high altitude natives

63. Which of the following evolutionary consequences do you believe will occur based upon the data in these populations?

    (A)   Tibetan women who produce many surviving offspring are more likely to have the high oxygen saturation genotype than the low oxygen saturation genotype.
    (B)   There is no oxygen saturation heritability in the Tibetan population.
    (C)   Ethiopian highlanders have two genes that can be inherited to improve oxygen saturation.
    (D)   Andean women with a low oxygen saturation genotype are more common in the population.

GRID-IN QUESTIONS

Following the multiple choice section, there are six math-based questions where you will complete a numeric grid for the answer. You will not be given multiple choice answers. You will calculate the answer and then bubble in the value on a scantron sheet.

Energy moves through trophic levels. A simple food chain is given that shows the feeding relationships in an old world field.

Viburnum bush → Tree hopper → Blue Jay → Red Tail Hawk

1. There are 5.65×10^{34} joules of energy stored in the viburnum bush population. How much energy is stored in the bodies of the tree hopper population?

2. There are 5.65×10^{34} joules of energy stored in the viburnum bush population. How much energy is stored in the bodies of the red tail hawk population?

A widow's peak is a human trait that results in a peak along the hairline in humans. This trait occurs due to simple Mendelian inheritance. The widow's peak trait is dominant and the straight hairline is recessive. In a human sample of 12000, 8678 have a widow's peak.

3. What is the frequency for the heterozygous genotype for widow's peak in this sample?

4. How many individuals in this sample are heterozygous for this condition?

Acetylcholine is a neurotransmitter that binds to the surface of skeletal muscle to cause skeletal muscle contraction. The contraction process ends when an enzyme called aceytlcholinesterase breaks down the acetylcholine. A graph is shown that shows how temperature can affect an enzyme like acetylcholinesterase and its ability to break down acetylcholine.

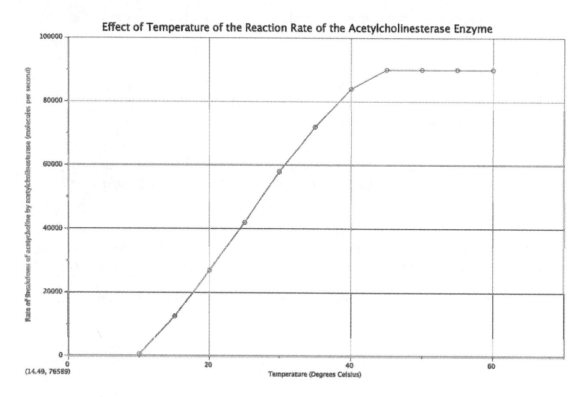

5. As the temperature has increased, the reaction rate increased. Calculate the slope of the line between 20 degrees Celsius and 40 degrees Celsius.

6. What temperature caused the denaturation of the of the acetylcholinesterase enzyme?

FREE-RESPONSE SECTION

Directions: In this section, the longer questions are worth 10 points. Smaller questions can be worth 2, 3, 4 or 6 points.

1. (10 point question) Proteins are large organic molecules with complicated three dimensional structures.

    a.   Explain how amino acids are used to build proteins.

    b.   Explain how the structure of a protein affects its function.

    c.   Select three proteins from the list and describe how the structure of that specific protein affects its function.

        i.   Hemoglobin
        ii.   Insulin
        iii.   Calcitonin
        iv.   Transcription factor
        v.   Blood clotting factor
        vi.   Epinephrine

2.   (10 point question) The graph below shows the population size of three different
     ground snakes in the southwestern desert. In this community, the sand snake and
     vipor snake were present when first records were recorded in 1900. The rattlesnake
     was introduced by human travellers in the 1950s.

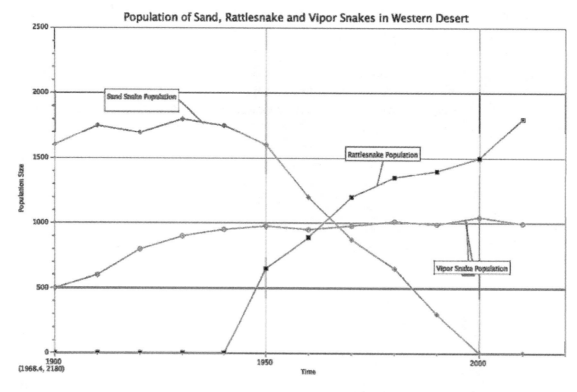

     a.   Explain the trends in the growth in each snake population over this 110 year
          time period.
     b.   Explain how the introduction of the rattlesnake into this desert affected the
          population of the sand snake and the vipor snake in this community.
     c.   What effect can introduced species have on the structure of a community?
     d.   What could be done to reestablish the sand snake population in this ecosystem?

3.   (4 point question) Charles Darwin sailed on the HMS Beagle and travelled all over
     the world gathering data that he recorded in a book called the Origin of Species. In
     this book, he documents how the global evidence supports a theory of a evolution by
     natural selection.

     a.   Explain evolution by natural selection.
     b.   Select a pair of closely-related organisms and describe how that pair gives
          evidence for evolution by natural selection.

4. (4 point question) Animal hormones are chemicals that travel through the bloodstream to reach their target cell. Many hormones have antagonists that help to regulate the body processes that they control.

   a. Select one pair of hormones from the given pairs. Give the function of each hormone in the pair in humans.

      i. Insulin . . . glucagon
      ii. Calcitonin . . . parathyroid hormone
      iii. Antidiuretic hormone . . . aldosterone

   b. Explain how the two hormones antagonize one another for overall homeostatic balance.

5. (6 point question) Analyze this graph that shows the rate of the breakdown of acetylcholine by acetylcholinesterase when exposed to a different temperatures.

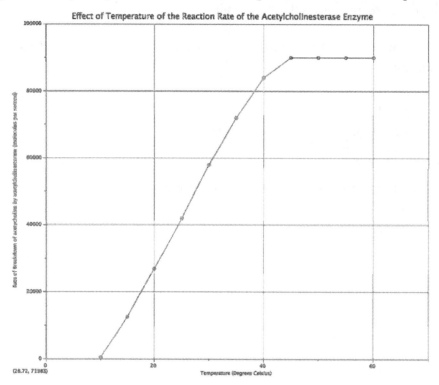

a. Explain why the rate of reaction increased between 20 and 40 degrees Celsius?
b. Explain why the rate of reaction reached a plateau at 50 degrees Celsius?
c. Explain what would happen if there was another molecule with a shape similar to the acetylcholine substrate in the environment.

6. (3 point question) Algae were grown in a closed tank. The dissolved oxygen level in the tank was measured every 3 hours for a two-day span. The tank was exposed to ample sunlight.

a. What will happen to the dissolved oxygen level during this time?
b. What is happening in the algae to affect the dissolved oxygen level? Describe the chemical events occurring in the chloroplasts of the algae that are affecting the oxygen concentration.

7.   (3 point question) DNA and RNA are two forms of nucleic acid molecules. Compare the structure of RNA to DNA. Describe both the similarities and the differences in the structures of DNA and RNA.

8.   (3 point question) The overall earth's temperatures have been steadily rising since the Industrial Revolution. The earth is experiencing a phenomena known as global climate change.

   a.   How is an increase in carbon dioxide connected to the climate change?
   b.   How have humans impacted the global carbon dioxide concentration?